VEDIC STORIES

Retold and Illustrated by Ananta Shakti Dasa

Other Publications by Touchstone Media:

Bhaktīvinoda Vānī Vaibhava
Prārthanā
Śrī Prema Bhaktī-candrikā
Sārvabhauma Śataka
Hari Bhaktī Kalpa Latika
Śrī Nityānanda-caritāmrta
Pāda Sevana
Sweet Pastimes of Damodara
The Dog and the Wolf
Great Heroes of the Mahābhārata Series
Krishna Pocket Guide
Amrta Vānī
Śrī Prema Vilāsa
Uddhava Gītā
Adventures of India Series
Śrī Krishna Vijaya
Mahābhārata
Bhagavad-gītā at a Glance
Vrindāvana, the Playground of God
Patrāmrta
Heart and Soul Connection
Śrīmati's Vegetarian Delight
Gita Stories from Padma Purana
Vaktrtavalī
Śrī Sarasvatī Sanlapa
Śrī Ksetra, Vaikuntha on Earth
Śrīmad Bhāgavatam, Symphony of Commentaries on the Tenth Canto
Pauranic Charitavali
Sri Kalki Purana
The Lord Appears as a Fish and Other Incarnations

If you are interested in the purchasing or the distribution of this book or any of the above publications, you may contact:

Touchstone Media
Vrindavan 281121, INDIA
www.touchstonemedia.com
e-mail : sales@touchstonemedia.com

Dedication

Dedicated to His Dvine Grace A. C. Bhaktivedanta Swami Prabhupada who sacrificed so much to uplfit the humanity.

I am hopeful that he will be a little pleased with this attempt to offer a glimpse of the Vedic culture to the children of the world upon whose shoulders rest our hopes for the future

Acknowledgements

I am much indebted to Karuna Dharani Devi dasi whose collaboration inspired me to start this book. Many thanks also go to Jayaradhe Devi dasi and Isodhyan dasi for their invaluable typing services, and to Rasamandala das for enhancing the stories with skilful editing and providing an introduction to them. Special thanks must go to my wife Vrajabhumi Devi dasi for indicating through her keen eyes how to improve the illustrations.

ISBN: 978-81-937276-2-1

Foreword

Veda literally means 'knowledge', but more specifically refers to the Sanskrit writings of ancient India. Previously this wisdom was transmitted orally, only being written down some fifty centuries ago. The author of the Vedas, a sage named Vyasa, divided this knowledge, both spiritual and mundane, into four parts. He later compiled the Puranas, often referred to as 'the fifth Veda'. The Puranas include a history of the ancient Indian world. Although of historical interest, the Puranas are not presented chronologically, nor are their accounts confined to this planet or our limited spheres of perception and comprehension. Vyasa purposefully arranged and presented them in a way that would broaden our awareness. It is from these popular yet profound texts that most of the stories retold in this book have originated.

Vyasa had many students who became teachers of Vedic wisdom. These spiritual masters then took their own disciples, and thus, through the process of disciplic succession, this knowledge was passed down throughout the ages. In modern times, His Divine Grace A.C Bhaktivedanta Swami Prabhupada is the foremost authority on Vedic philosophy, religion and culture. His translations of the Vedic texts, with extensive commentary, are used as standard textbooks in colleges and universities throughout the world. He also established a worldwide confederation of farms, schools, temples, colleges and cultural centres. One of his prime ambitions was that children might benefit from Vedic truths and values, as they are universal and go beyond all sectarian concern. The publisher hope that this volume will be a small step in that direction.

Though this book was initially written for children belonging to the Vedic (Hindu) tradition, we are hopeful they will be an inspiration to the children from all walks of life and that they will be of particular interest to those involved in religious, personal and moral education.

---- Rasamandala Dasa

Contents

Buddha The Teacher

Many years ago, in a small kingdom, in Nepal, north of India, there lived a king called Shuddhodan.

One night his wife, Queen Maya, Had an amazing dream. She dreamt that she was carried away by angels to a golden house high in the mountains. There she was bathed and laid on a silken bed where a white elephant with six tusks and holding a lotus in its trunk came to her. As it touched her right side with

the lotus flower, a baby entered her womb. Queen Maya awoke and excitedly told her husband about the dream.

The king called his wisest ministers to explain the meaning of this dream. They said it foretold that a great person would soon be born. "Either he will become a saintly king or a great religious teacher".

And just as they said, a baby was born from the queen's right side, a baby who could stand up and speak just after being born. The brahmin priests who were consulted after the birth noted thirty-two special marks on the baby's body. His ear lobes were long, and in the

lines of his feet they saw eight-spoked wheels. They confirmed that according to tradition these were signs of a great person.

The parents named the child Siddhartha, which means 'he who brings goodness'. From birth Siddhartha was kind and gentle. He avoided playing rough games with other boys and spent much of his childhood alone or talking to his pets. Even wild deer would eat from his hands. The king protected him from the outside world, ensuring that Siddhartha grew up happily in the palace grounds, and never experienced any of life's miseries.

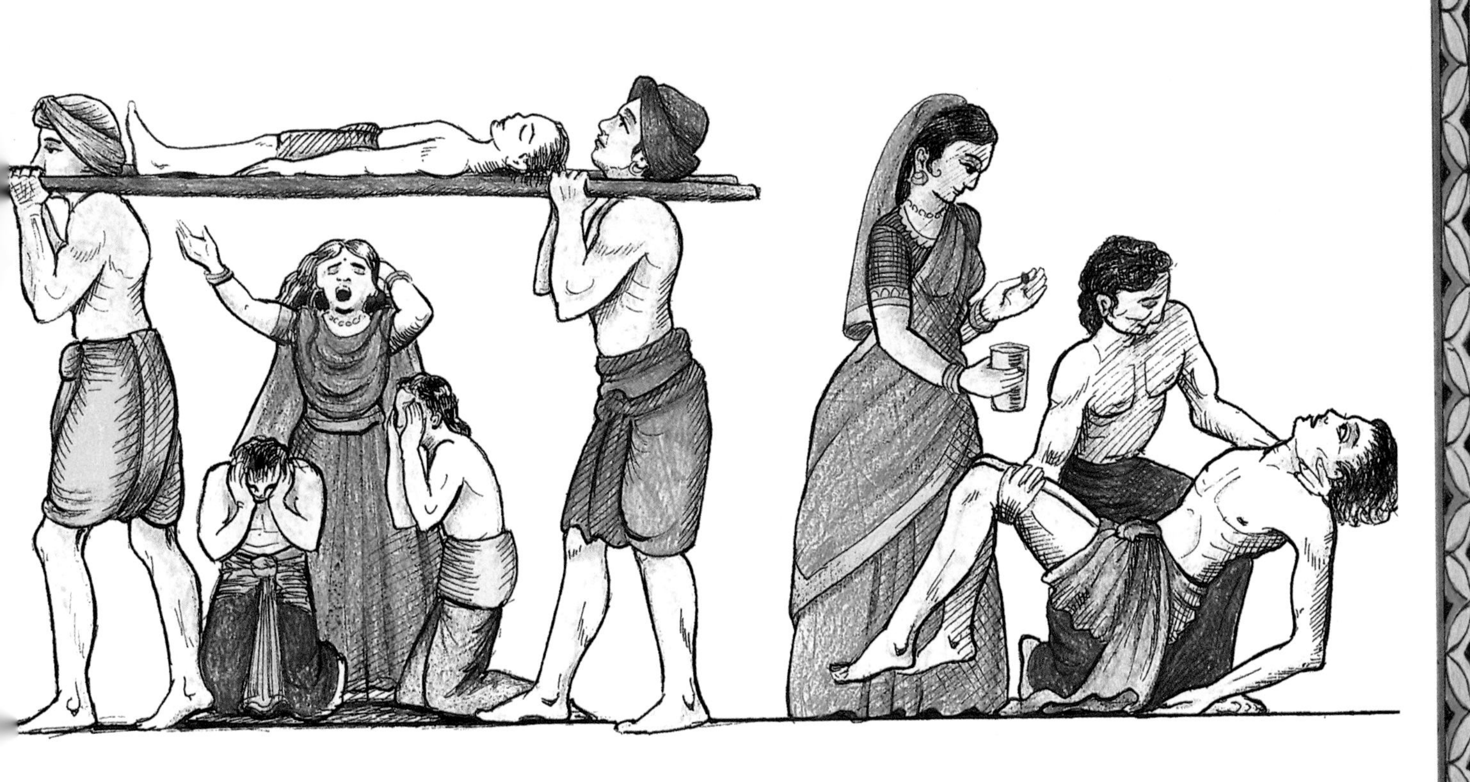

It wasn't until Siddhartha was twenty-nine that he left the palace grounds for the first time. As he passed along the road on his chariot, he saw a bent and wrinkled man, hobbling with a stick. The prince felt stunned. Then he spied, on a veranda, a man lying in bed and groaning in agony. Siddhartha felt pain in his heart as never before. But when he saw a corpse borne on a stretcher and surrounded by weeping people, he became almost mad with curiosity.

A wandering monk was also passing by, Siddhartha eagerly approached him and pleaded for an explanation, "What have I seen. Why do such things happen?"

The holy man told the prince that he had just witnessed old age, disease and death. He explained that everyone born in this world meets these three things at some time in their life.

Siddhartha decided that he must find a solution to these problems. So when he returned to the palace he resolved to become a hermit.

Without a word to anyone, he left for the forest. There he practised severe austerities. He fasted from eating for long periods of time. However,

Siddhartha's mind was still troubled. He eventually felt that starving his body wasn't the way to find the answers he wanted. So, he gave up his austerities, being now careful to eat and sleep just the right amount, neither too much nor too little.

One day, while sitting in silent meditation beneath a bo tree, he attained the peace of mind and answers for which he had sought so long. From then on, he was known as Buddha, 'the awakened one'.

Out of humility, Buddha felt unqualified to teach this understanding to others. But then, in a vision, the creator, Lord Brahma, requested him to share his knowledge with others. So, Buddha went out amongst the people. He taught them that all suffering comes from desire, and if we want to get free from suffering we have to become free from selfish desires. He taught ahimsa, the principle of avoiding harm to others. "We must love and respect all living creatures," he instructed, "and in this way develop wisdom and kindness."

Buddha gathered many disciples, and His fame as a spiritual leader spread far and wide. He instructed his followers not to eat meat. In this way he prevented the killing of innocent animals throughout India and beyond.

At the age of eighty, on the very same day of the year on which he was born and also on which he attained enlightenment, Buddha returned to the spiritual world. Buddhists today celebrate this day with a festival called Wesak. On this day, in shrines all over the world, people worship the beautiful image of Lord Buddha with incense and flowers.

The Brahmin And The Cobbler

Narada Muni, the sage of the gods, was once approached by old Jara, the daughter of Time. She wanted to marry him, but he refused her. Greatly offended, Jara cursed him that he would never have a fixed place to live. As a result, he is constantly travelling, playing on his stringed instrument, the vina, as he chants the holy name of the Supreme Lord, Narayan.

During his travels, Narada once came across a proud brahmin priest who had just finished his daily fire sacrifice. Seeing the famous sage, the brahmin greeted him, "Namaste, my dear Narada."

"If you are going to the spiritual world," requested the priest, "then please do me a favour. Ask Lord Narayan when I'm going to join Him there. I think it should be very soon, but I'd like to verify it anyway."

"All right", agreed Narada, "I'll ask Him."

The next day Narada passed a humble cobbler, the lowest of the castes, repairing shoes on the roadside. "All glories to you, Narada Muni," the cobbler called out.

"All glories to the devotees of Lord Narayan," returned Narada. "And, how are you?"

"By the grace of the Lord," responded the cobbler, "all is well. But speaking of the Lord, will you be seeing Him soon?"

"Oh yes," replied Narada. "But why do you ask? Do you want me to speak to Him on your behalf?"

"Oh yes," answered the cobbler. "You see, I'm very tired of living in this material world. Please would you ask the Lord how many more lifetimes I have to wait before going back to the spiritual world?"

"Yes. I'll certainly do that for you," replied the sage.

Narada, who has a spiritual body, then left for the spiritual world to see Lord Narayan. Upon arriving he bowed his head to the lotus feet of the Lord.

Narayan received him with honor and affection. "How are you, dear Narada? Is there anything I can do for you?"

"By Your mercy all is well, my Lord," Narada replied. He then spoke of both the brahmin and the cobbler, putting forward their questions.

Lord Narayan, who knows everything-past, present and future- then informed Narada, "The brahmin will be returning to Me only after one hundred lifetimes. But I will see the cobbler at the end of his present life."

Narada was surprised at this answer since it is traditionally considered that brahmins are elevated, while cobblers are lowly because they make shoes from the skins of dead animals.

Narayan smiled. "When you see the brahmin and the cobbler they will both ask what I was doing. Tell them I was threading an elephant through the eye of a needle. By their reactions to this, you will understand everything."

Intrigued by the Lord's words, Narada left immediately. Arriving at the house of the brahmin, he told him he would have to wait one hundred lifetimes. The arrogant brahmin was visibly shocked. "One hundred lifetimes! I don't believe you even saw Narayan. Tell me what He was doing."

"Threading an elephant through the eye of a needle." Replied Narada. "Threading an elephant through the eye of

a needle?" spluttered the brahmin. "IMPOSSIBLE! No one can do such a thing. You are lying to me. You are probably lying to me about the one hundred lifetimes as well."

Unperturbed, Narada took his leave and went to visit the cobbler. He conveyed Narayana's message that soon he would he returning to the spiritual realm.

"I will go back to the spiritual world at the end of this life?" exclaimed the cobbler in great joy. "How merciful the Lord is! But my dear Narada, please tell me what my Lord was doing, and thus bring pleasure to my heart."

"Why, the Lord was threading an elephant through the eye of a needle," Narada answered.

"Wonderful! Wonderful!" exclaimed the cobbler.

"You actually believe that?" Narada asked.

"Why, yes, of course," the cobbler said without hesitation. "See that big oak tree across the road? It came from just an acorn. So if the Lord can pack a huge oak tree into such a seed, He can easliy thread an elephant through the eye of a needle."

Seeing the difference between the proud brahmin and the humble cobbler, Narada easily understood why they were to be rewarded in different ways.

The Intelligent Minister

Five hundred years ago, Birbal was prime minister of Emperor Akbar's court. Although his wisdom and sense of humour made him popular, other members of the court were jealous of Birbal's position.One day the Emperor overheard some of these criticisms. They claimed that they had to work very hard, while Birbal just seemed to sit around all day. They felt that any one of them could do a better job than him.

Akbar explained that it took special qualifications to be his chief adviser. However, he saw that his courtiers were not convinced. So, calling for his royal elephant, he announced to his court, "I have a test for you all. Whoever can give me the exact weight of this elephant will be my next chief minister."

Birbal's rivals did not know where to start. Scratching their heads, they looked at each other with puzzled expressions. Then they huddled together and discussed the problem. Finally, with shamed faces, they turned out to the emperor, "It is not possible to do, Emperor Akbar."

Akbar turned to Birbal, "Can you complete this task?"

"Certainly, your Majesty," Birbal replied and led the elephant away.

When he was out of sight, one of his enemies boldly spoke out, "If between us we couldn't figure out a way to do this, what can he do alone?" The others muttered words of agreement, but the Emperor remained silent.

An hour later Birbal returned. "The elephant weighs 4992 pounds," he announced.

The mouths of the other ministers gaped open and their eyes widened in disbelief. They whispered among themselves, "He just made that number up." "He must be lying." "It can't be done."

The Emperor then asked Birbal, "How do you know the weight?" "Did you get a large set of scales?"

"No, your Majesty," answered Birbal. "The elephant is too heavy to be weighed like that. I took him to the river, put him on a boat and marked the waterline. Then, after taking him ashore, I filled the boat with sacks of grain. We already knew how much each sack weighed. Once the waterline was again reached, I counted the number of sacks. In this way I was able to calculate the elephant's weight."

Turning to his courtiers, the Emperor cautioned them, "Now do you understand? One who is wise gets more done with little effort. Birbal deserves to be my chief minister."

And they had to agree.

The Plover's Eggs

Once a pair of plovers lived by the shore of the mighty ocean. Whales, dolphins, turtles and all kinds of fish swam in those waters and along the shore were all varieties of crabs and water birds.

The hen plover laid her eggs in her nest near the shore and happily waited for her chicks to hatch.

Not long after, the spring tide came, raising the waters higher than usual. The ocean's watery hands swept away the poor bird's eggs. Though the plover cried in despair, the ocean paid no attention to her piteous calls.

Unable to bear the loss, and determined to recover her eggs, the heartbroken plover resolved to empty the ocean. She plucked out drops of water with her tiny beak, while beating her wings against the waves, as if to dry the waters up.

The fishes were amused. "What is she making so much fuss about?" one trout laughed. "We lay our eggs in the water with no problem at all."

The shore birds did not think it was so funny. They felt sorry for their sister bird. One gull said, "That ocean is so heartless. He should be taught a lesson."

"But what can we do?" asked another.

The great albatross spoke up. Not only was he the oldest of the birds, but the wisest as well, having flown far and wide and seen many things. "This ocean is not so great. Garuda is far more powerful. He is king of all birds, and the carrier of Lord Vishnu. He is the protector of the weak. Let's seek his help."

So, all birds gathered together and sang out in a rousing chorus.

Hearing the cries, Garuda, the giant eagle, flew from the heavenly sky, his huge wings humming the sound of Vedic hymns. The birds' breasts swelled in great joy as their famous relative landed on the beach. His brilliant body glowed with spiritual energy. His sharp beak and talons gave the birds confidence but struck with fear into the hearts of snakes and envious people.

The King of Birds witnessed the plover's determination to empty the ocean. Feeling

compassion for his small sister, he rose high into the air, his body casting dark shadows over the waves. "O miserly ocean," he boomed, "I demand you return the plover's egg, lest I myself take up her task."

Upon hearing these words, the ocean and its residents trembled in fear. They knew that if he wished, Garuda could swallow them all up in one go. So, to pacify him, the ocean carried the plover's eggs on its waves and returned them to their rightful owner.

The delighted plover took her eggs and moved the nest to a safer place along the shore. All the other birds helped her with much cheering and sweet singing.

Later, when they all finished, and the moon was rising, the wise old albatross called everyone together. "Our sister the plover overcame disaster by the strength of her unflinching determination. Let this be a lesson to us all."

It was the second day of the harvest festival. Already the villagers had made offering of fruits, grains and flowers to the demigods in charge of the rain, sun and moon.

They were looking forward to the next day, when Gopal, the village Deity, would be carried in procession around the village and worshipped with much pomp and ceremony. That was to be followed with feasting and dancing.

But the festive mood was spoiled when everyone heard that the night before someone in the village had been going around stealing valuables.

This was brought to the attention of Shrutidhar, the village elder. As night fell, he gathered the village people around the fire. In front of him he held a blackened pot.

"One amongst us is a thief", he announced. "And to catch him or her I have made a fire from the wood of a thief-catching tree. I have chanted the necessary mantras (prayers) to bring out the power of the tree which

is now on this pot in the form of black ash. This special soot will only mark the hand of the thief. No one else."

The villagers whispered excitedly amongst themselves as Shrutidhar passed them the pot. Each pressed forward to touch the pot.

Finally, the pot was passed back to the elder. "Anyone else?" Shrutidhar asked, "Have we missed anyone?"

There was no reply.

Shrutidhar then lit a torch and requested everyone to file past, palms outstretched. One after another they showed blackened hands. Shrutidhar, however, remained silent.

But when he saw a pair of white hands, he proclaimed, "O villagers, here is your thief!"

Falling to his knees, the man begged, "Please, have mercy on me!"

The people looked on in astonishment as the village constable led the crook away.

Shrutidhar explained, "I made up the story about the thief-catching tree. You all only have ordinary tree ash on your hands. However, believing my words, the thief was the only person afraid to touch the pot."

After he returned all the valuables, the thief was forgiven, and so the festival could continue. Everyone praised Shrutidhar's wisdom.

Anjaneya Eats The Sun

One day while watching monkeys play on the beautiful slopes of Kailash Mountain, the great god Shiva and is wife Parvati wanted to do the same. So, they transformed themselves into monkeys and enjoyed swinging from the branches of trees and picking up juicy fruits in the forest. They stayed as monkeys only for a little while, but when they returned to their divine forms Parvati received a great shock. She realized that she had become pregnant. A little while later she gave birth to a baby monkey.

Seeing his wife so upset, Shiva called for Vayu, the wind god. "Take this baby away. Please find someone else to take care of him."

Because Vayu is the wind god and blows everywhere, he knows everything. He knew of a race of intelligent monkey people, the Vanaras, living deep in the Kishkinda forest. He also knew that their rulers, King Keshari and Queen Anjana, were unhappy at being childless.

So, while the king and queen were sitting in the temple praying to God for a child, the invisible Vayu placed the baby monkey on Queen Anjana's lap. Overjoyed at having their prayers answered, the king and queen called the baby prince "Anjaneya", (the son of Anjana).

The monkey child grew extremely fast, must faster than any normal child. His appetite also grew, and his mother had a difficult time finding enough food to feed him. One day he cried, "I'm still hungry. What more can I eat?"

His mother had no more food. But she thought that he was big enough to find fruits in the forest for himself. So, she pointed at the sun in the twilight sky. "I have no food here for you, my son. But if you like you can search out fruits for yourself in the forest. You will know which fruits are good to eat because any fruit that is red like the sun will be ripe."

Anjaneya was a clever boy. He said, "Thank you for your advice mother. But most of the fruits in the forest are so little. The sun is red; therefore, it

must be ripe. And it is a very large fruit, isn't it? Surely that will satisfy my hunger."

His mother tried to explain that this was not a good idea, but Anjaneya did not listen to her. With the power of his father, Shiva and of Vayu, the wind god, he leapt high into the sky, growing to an enormous size.

The sun god was speeding across the sky, seated on his fiery chariot pulled by eight shining horses. Anjaneya simply reached out, seized them all and thrust them into his mouth. The entire sky darkened.

Indra, the king of heaven, asked Agni, the fire god, "What's caused this sudden darkness?"

"Something must be blocking the sun. Throw your thunderbolt at it," Agni suggested.

So, Indra unleashed his terrible thunderbolt weapon, sending it hurtling through the sky. Then, mounting his tusked elephant and guided by the light of the stars, he sped towards the sun.

The thunderbolt had struck Anjaneya on the side of his face, injuring his jaw. Anjaneya pulled the weapon from his cheek, keeping the sun within his mouth.

When Indra arrived, he saw this gigantic monkey holding his thunderbolt weapon. Confused, he ran to Brahma, the grandfather of the gods.

But when he told Brahma what he had seen, Brahma smiled. "This monkey has the strength of Shiva—so you cannot force him to open his mouth. You can only ask him nicely if he would please give us back the sun."

So, Brahma, Indra, Agni and Vayu, along with millions of other demigods, approached Anjaneya. "Please", they begged, "Open your mouth."

"Why should I?" the monkey replied through his clenched teeth.

"If you do, you will live a long life," said Brahma.

"If you do, you will become the most famous of all," Indra said.

"If you do, fire will not burn you," said Agni.

"If you do, you will be as fast as the wind," said Vayu.

But Anjaneya, unimpressed, continued to hold the sun in his mouth; he did not care for their blessings. What he wanted right now was for his jaw to stop hurting.

Brahma could read Anjaneya's mind. He said, "Anjaneya, I know how to mend your jaw."

Anjaneya looked at him doubtfully- was this a trick?

But Brahma poured water from his magical water pot on Anjaneya's cheek and at once it stopped hurting. Anjaneya smiled at him.

Then Brhaspati, the wise priest of the gods, stepped forward. "We know that you are hungry, Anjaneya, and that's why you have tried to eat the sun."

Anjaneya nodded his head. He could still feel his stomach growling.

Brhaspati said, "The sun is not good food. In fact, it is not food at all. We would like to give you the blessing that with ease you can gather fruits from all over the world to satisfy your hunger."

Anjaneya still did not release the sun from his mouth, but he tilted his head to one side as if considering this offer.

Brhaspati continued, "As well as this we will benedict you with knowledge of the use of herbs. From these plants you'll be able to make all types of medicine."

Thinking these to be suitable blessings, Anjaneya consented to open his mouth. With a flood of light, the glorious sun-god flew out on his blazing chariot. The sky became radiantly bright once more.

From that day on Anjaneya was called Hanuman, or "one with a mended jaw". Hanuman indeed ate many wonderful fruits and knew all about healing herbs. He became famous throughout India and throughout the world, as the bravest servant of the glorious King Ramachandra. But that is another story.

Again Become A Mouse

In a small clearing deep in the forest a mystic yogi sat absorbed in meditation. Sitting on the ground with crossed legs and with closed eyes the yogi was as still as a statue. He was appreciating the calm and peace surrounding him.

Without warning, a frightened mouse jumped into the yogi's lap. He squeaked, "Please save me. A cat is chasing me."

The yogi slowly opened one eye then the other. He peered down at the mouse. "It's not my business to go chasing cats."

"Please sir, please help me," the mouse squeaked.

"All right," the yogi said. "You can become a cat." Then he waved a hand, and cast a spell, and the mouse became a cat.

The cat dashed away, back into the forest.

A few days later, the yogi was sitting, as always, in peaceful meditation. This time a cat crept from the bushes. It was meowing pitifully, "Please save me! A ferocious dog is after me."

The yogi said, "I recognize you. You're the mouse I changed into a cat the other day."

The cat meowed louder.

"Well, well, what shall we do this time?" Then he cast another spell and transformed the cat into a big barking dog.

The dog ran into the jungle, and the yogi continued his meditation.

A couple of days later the dog returned, in a very distressed condition. He ran up to the yogi, panting and whimpering, "Please help me. A great tiger is chasing me."

The kind yogi considered the plight of the terrified dog. He replied, "Oh you are such a fearful creature. Stop shaking. You too will be a tiger. Have no more fear." With that he cast a spell and the dog turned into the most dangerous beast in the forest.

But instead of going away, the tiger paced around proudly, admiring His new body. He licked his black and orange striped coat with his long tongue, and with great satisfaction examined his razor-sharp claws.

When the yogi noticed the tiger eyeing him, he said, "So, tiger, what do you want now?"

With a sly smile, the tiger replied, "I want to eat you". He made ready to pounce.

The yogi was too quick for him. Pointing his finger, he cast another spell. "Ungrateful wretch! Again, become a mouse!"

Bhrigu's Footprint

One day on Maharloka, a planet beyond the pole star, many mystic saints gathered together. They happily discussed the mysteries of life-talking about the soul, reincarnation and the law of karma. However, they could not agree on who was the greatest person in the whole cosmos.

Some said, "It must be Brahma, because he is the creator."

Others disagreed, "No, Vishnu, the preserver, is the greatest." Still others maintained, "Shiva must be supreme, since he destroys everything."

This debate continued at length until Bhrigu Muni came up with an idea. "I propose that I visit all three of these great personalities- Brahma, Vishnu and Shiva. I will test them in such a way that we can understand who is the greatest." Everyone agreed.

And so, using his mystic powers of travel, Bhrigu first went to the planet of his father, the four-headed Brahma. Entering the palace, he walked straight up to his father without showing the slightest respect. He stood there, staring at him as if to challenge his authority.

Brahma's body shook in anger. His eyebrows knitted together, his nostrils flared and his eyes turned copper-red. It was evident that it was only with the greatest effort that he was able to contain his anger. So Bhrigu excused himself and quickly left.

He next visited Mount Kailash in the Himalayas, the home of his brother, Lord Shiva. Shiva greeted him with open arms. "Bhrigu, what a nice surprise! It's been so long."

Bhrigu, however, shrank back in disgust. "Don't dare touch me. You're so dirty. You wear snakes around your neck and arms, and you smear your body with ash from the crematorium. Keep away from me."

Shiva seized his trident and screamed, "How dare you insult me! For that you will die!" He started dancing wildly and beating his drum, just as he does at the time of universal destruction.

Just as Shiva was about to release his deadly trident, his wife Parvati stepped in. "Oh please, my Lord, forgive him. He is both your brother and a brahmin. You will spoil your good name if you kill him."

Shiva was pacified by her gentle soothing words. Though still breathing heavily, he put his trident down, allowing Bhrigu to leave alive. On his way to Vishnuloka, Bhrigu considered, "I have offended my father with bad manners and my brother with cruel words. I shall have to do something even worse when I see Vishnu."

Lord Vishnu and His queen Lakshmi were joking and smiling with each other. They didn't even appear to notice Their uninvited guest approaching.

Pretending to be upset, Bhrigu strode up to Vishnu and planted a very hard kick on His chest. He shouted, "How dare You ignore me!" As if mildly surprised, Vishnu looked up. He merely smiled. "Please forgive Me, Bhrigu. Has your delicate foot become bruised after contacting My hard chest?" He took Bhrigu's foot in His hands, "Please let Me massage it for you."

Lakshmi, however, was not so forgiving. She said, "Personally I will tolerate an insult. But I will never tolerate one against my Lord. I curse you that from this day on all brahmins such as yourself will be penniless." Bhrigu considered that the goal of life was simply to please Lord Vishnu, and he knew that love of money can often be the root of evil. So he took the curse to be a blessing. And so, with the Lord's permission, Bhrigu left Vishnuloka feeling great satisfaction.

Upon his return the other saints listened spellbound as he related what had happened. They all agreed that Vishnu was full of tolerance, mercy and all other virtues. He was therefore the greatest person of all. And from that time on although pious brahmins remain relatively poor, Lord Vishnu has borne the footprint of Bhrigu on His sacred chest.

The Lake Of Death

There once lived five princes known as the Pandavas, the sons of King Pandu. One time, while they were living in the forest, a brahmin (priest) came to them for help.

"Maharaj Yudisthira, you must help," he begged of the eldest Pandava. "The arani sticks from which I make fire have been taken. A deer came into my hut, caught up the sticks in its horns, and ran away. Without fire I cannot perform my daily religious duties."

So, the Pandavas went out to search for the deer. They quickly spotted it, but it ran away. Hour after hour they pursued the nimble deer but were unable to capture it. Finally, overtaken by exhaustion and thirst, they rested in the cool shade of a tree.

Yudisthira spoke to his youngest brother, "Nakula, we need water. Climb this tree and see if there is a river in sight."

Nakula, although tired, climbed high into the tree. "Yes, I see a lake nearby," he shouted, much to the relief of the others.

"Good", Yudisthira croaked, his throat parched with thirst. "Please, would you fetch us some water?"

Nakula ran to the lake. He could almost taste the cooling waters refreshing his dry mouth.

He knelt down and was raising a palmful of water to his mouth, when a loud voice boomed out. "Stop! Do not take a drink until you have answered my question. I am the keeper of this lake. If you don't do as I say then you will die."

Completely exhausted, Nakula decided to ignore the mysterious voice. He took a large gulp of the cool water-immediately fell down dead.

Meanwhile the other Pandavas were waiting for what seems like ages. Each minute made their thirst more desperate.

So Yudisthira begged another brother, "Sahadeva, would you please help Nakula bring back the water?"

Sahadeva practically crawled to the lake and was shocked to find his brother dead. But his own throat now burning with thirst, he rushed to the water's edge.

Again, the voice ordered him to stop.

Sahadeva, ignored the advice and scooped up a palmful of water. Like his brother, he dropped dead on the spot.

Yudisthira next sent to Arjuna, and then some time later, Bheema. Neither of them returned.

Yudisthira, now understanding that something was terribly wrong, went himself. He could scarcely believe his eyes. The lifeless bodies of four powerful warriors lay scattered by the shore of the lake. How could they be killed so easily with no sign of a fight?

He sank to his knees in grief. It was not possible for him to live without his faithful brothers. They had sacrificed so much to please him, and now they were gone forever. Then his own fierce thirst overcame his anguish, and he crawled towards the cool refreshing water.

"Stop!" the voice called out ominously. "You cannot drink this water until you've answered my questions. Heed this warning or you'll meet the same fate as your brothers."

Yudisthira stopped and, scanning the sky, replied, "I'll do as you request to the best of my ability. But before I do, please show yourself to me. I am astonished how a single person has the power to kill all four of my brothers. Bheema himself had the strength of ten thousand elephants. Not even a god has the power to kill any one of my brothers."

A mighty and frightening Yaksha, a magician, appeared before the prince.

With respect, Yudisthira joined his palms and bowed slightly before the sorcerer. "Thank you. Please ask me your questions."

"Your humility is charming," the Yaksha said. "Here is my first question: What is faster than the wind?"

Without hesitation Yudisthira replied, "The mind of course."

The Yaksha rubbed his hands together. "Quite right. But do you know what the most valuable possession is?"

"That's also easy- it's knowledge."

"Aha", said the Yaksha. "But what is real knowledge?"

"True knowledge is knowledge of the divine," Yudisthira replied.

"Yes, that is right," the Yaksha agreed. "Now tell me what makes something agreeable only when it is given up?"

Yudisthira looked first at the enticing water and then to his dead brothers. "It can only be pride."

"And what is wickedness?" the Yaksha challenged.

"Speaking ill of others," Yudisthira said.

"But do you know what charity is?" the Yaksha asked.

Yudisthira looked over to his brothers lying dead on the lakeside. With tears in his eyes he said, "Charity is giving protection to all creatures."

The Yakshas smiled wryly, also looking at the dead men, and noting how Yudisthira was licking his own lips in what must have been unbearable thirst. He then asked, "What is patience?"

Yudisthira drew his eyes away from the cool waters of the lake and tried to ignore the increasing dryness in his throat. He took a deep breath and said, "Patience can only be the ability to control the senses."

"Yes," the Yakshas continued. "But now for my last question: What is the most wonderful thing in the world?"

Yudisthira considered carefully before answering this final question. He glanced once again over at his dead brothers. With confidence he said, "Day after day living beings are entering the house of death. No one escapes it, but those remaining think they will not die. Can there be anything more wonderful than this?"

The Yaksha smiled broadly. "I am satisfied by your intelligent answers," he said. You are the wisest person alive and deserve to take a boon from me. I grant you the life of one of your brothers. Please choose which one."

After pausing to consider, Yudisthira replied, "I choose Nakula."

"But why Nakula?" enquired the Yaksha. "Why not the mighty Bheema or Arjuna? They surely are more valuable to you?"

Yudisthira explained, "My father had two wives, Kunti and Madri. Bheema, Arjuna and I are Kunti's sons. So for Madri's benefit I choose Nakula."

Overjoyed at hearing such a selfless answer, the Yaksha brought all the dead brothers back to life. He then revealed to Yudisthira his true identity. "I am your father, the God of Death. I'm also called Dharma, the knower of what is right and what is wrong. I wanted to test your wisdom. I am proud that you answered so well. My son, because you are devoted to truth and righteousness, you will never know defeat."

Yudisthira humbly fell down at his father's feet and wept tears of joy.

The Challenge

Once the ruling king of India passed a law that anyone defeated in a debate with his court pandit (scholar) had to pay a yearly tax, or else execution. Kolahala, the court pandit, was very proud that with his clever words he had defeated the learned teacher, Bhasyacharya.

For two years Bhasyacharya paid the fine, but now he didn't have enough money. One day he went away on a business trip, leaving a twelve-year-old student, Yamunacharya, alone in the school.

Two bullies arrived at the school and told Yamunacharya, "We are Kolahala's disciples. As you know, he is the greatest scholar. What you may not know is that your guru owes him some tax money. If he doesn't pay it by tomorrow, he'll be put to death."

Although usually of a gentle nature, Yamunacharya felt himself burning with anger. "You are both foolish disciples of a foolish master. Why should my noble teacher waste time with the likes of you? Go tell your teacher that I, who am but the lowest disciple of my guru, challenges him. Let him face me, if he dares!"

Speechless, Kolahala's disciples stormed out of the school. The king and the court pandit were amused when they heard the challenger's age. But understanding that Yamunacharya was serious, the king sent a carriage and an escort of soldiers to bring him to the palace.

By that time Bhasyacharya had returned. Upon hearing that his young student had challenged a pandit, whom he himself had not been able to beat, he was worried. Nevertheless, he could find no way to stop the contest.

News spread quickly, and a crowd gathered to watch the debate. The pious brahmins blessed the brave boy, "May you smash the pride of that cruel pandit just as Vishnu in the form of a dwarf defeated Bali, the demon king."

Even the Queen shared this attitude and, sensing intuitively that this would be the pandit's downfall, she addressed the king, "As a mountain of cloth is reduced to ashes by a mere spark, so the mountain-like pride of Kolahala will be destroyed by this young boy."

The king laughed at this, "I'll bet that you are wrong."

"All right," replied the queen. "If I am proven wrong, then I promise to become the servant of the maidservant."

The king raised his eyebrows in surprise, but with confidence met the wager. "All right, and if the boy wins, then half my kingdom will be his."

The queen nodded in agreement.

When everyone had taken their seats in the royal court, the king signalled for the contest to begin.

Kolahala asked one question after another, but Yamunacharya answered all of them easily.

The boy then commented, "You are asking simple questions just because you judge a person's learning by his size. If that's true, then a water buffalo must be more intelligent than you."

Restraining his anger, Kolahala twisted his mouth into a smile. "Well answered. So now it is your turn to put questions to me."

"Very well", responded Yamunacharya. "I will make three statements and you must prove that they are false. Do you accept this challenge?"

Kolahala, who was very expert at juggling words, nodded in approval.

"Firstly, I say that your mother is not a barren woman. Prove this to be wrong if you can."

Kolahala, considering that had his mother been barren he would not have been born, was unable to speak.

Yamunacharya spoke again, "Sir, as you appear to have no answer, I'll make a second statement for you to prove wrong. It is this: Our king is a most righteous person."

Kolahala's reddened face now turned white with anger; how could he deny the godly qualities of the king who was sitting there? Again, he remained painfully silent.

Yamunacharya again spoke. "Listen to my third statement and prove it wrong if you can. It is this: The good queen, present here today, is completely faithful to her husband."

Unable to speak against the queen, the defeated pandit exploded with rage. "You rogue, I will admit defeat only if you can prove your own statements to be wrong. Failing this, you should be executed for your insolence."

The crowd erupted, setting the entire palace in an uproar. Yamunacharya stood up, raised his hands high and cried out, "I will do it. I will prove all three statements to be wrong."

The crowd hushed.

The boy continued, "Firstly, I said that the pandit's mother was not barren. In the Manu Samhita, the lawbook of mankind, it is stated that a woman who has only one child is to be considered barren."

"Secondly, I said that the king is a most righteous man. According to the lawbooks a king takes credit for one sixth of the good acts performed by his subjects, but also has to answer for one sixth of their sinful acts. Therefore, although our king is sinless himself, out of duty he is burdened by the selfish deeds of his citizens."

"Regarding my third statement about our queen being faithful to her husband, I say this to refute it. According to Manu's laws the king represents the sun god, the air god, the fire god, the moon god, the god of death, the god of waters, the king of heaven, and the heavenly treasurer, Kuvera. Therefore, the queen is married not only to the king but to eight demigods. So how can she be called faithful?"

Everyone except Kolahala and his disciples clapped, cheered and marvelled at Yamunacharya's victory-especially the queen, who had now won her wager. The noble king embraced the boy, declaring, "You have defeated the proud Kolahala who wished you to die. Now you can do with him as you like for you are the rightful victor."

The saintly Yamunacharya, however, forgave the despondent pandit, took half of the kingdom, and above all, made his guru very happy.

The Sadhu's Blessings

A sadhu (saintly person) and his disciple were passing through a city. "Let us see whether we can make our journey a learning experience," he said to his disciple. By chance, the Prince of the kingdom was mounting his fine white stallion just as they were walking by.

"Greetings holy man," the prince called out. "Please give me your blessings."

Raising his palm, the sadhu replied, "May you live forever."

The prince galloped off, and the sadhu's disciple enquired, "Why did you bless him to live forever, master?"

The sadhu answered, "He is now enjoying a life of sense pleasure. However, he hunts animals for sport, so when he dies he'll suffer for this sin. So, it's best for him to live forever and stay as he is now."

"Live Forever"

"Die Now"

Later they saw a young student of spiritual science, a brahmachari, dressed in saffron cloth, collecting alms for his teacher. When he saw the sadhu, he touched his hands together and offered him respect.

In reply the sadhu said, "May you die immediately."

Again, the disciple queried, "Why did you curse him to die?"

The sadhu laughed. "That was not a curse, but a blessing. At present he is pure and sinless. However, if he continues to live his future is uncertain."

"Why is that?" the disciple asked.

"Because there is always the danger of falling into worldly ways. But if he dies right now, he will certainly be promoted to the higher worlds."

As they approached the market place the disciple had to hold his nose. The air was filled with a sickly smell of death coming from the corpses of

"Don't Live, Don't Die"

skinned animals, cut into pieces and hung on hooks in front of the butcher's shop.

A red-faced man, the shop owner, called out to the sadhu, "Hello! Any blessings for me today?"

Once again, the sadhu raised his palm. "Yes. I bless you that you neither live nor die."

The butcher scratched his head and muttered, "What a strange blessing."

After they left the market place the disciple enquired, "What did you mean by that greeting?"

"Don't you think the butcher is in a hellish condition right now?" the sadhu asked.

His disciple nodded.

"He has killed so many innocent animals that he will surely go to hell for many thousands of years," the sadhu explained. "So, he will suffer if he lives or if he dies."

Next, they passed a temple entrance where a devotee was offering her heartfelt prayers to the Supreme Lord. She did not even notice the sadhu approaching. But he called out, "May you live, or may you die."

"Let me guess why you said that," ventured the disciple. "Constantly remembering God, a devotee is always happy. Therefore, it makes no difference to her whether she lives or dies. She will go on remembering God in this life and in the next."

Smiling, the sadhu replied, "You are learning well."

"Live or Die"

A Bundle of Sticks

An old brahmin priest lived in a holy place, an ashram, with his seven disciples. They worshipped there some very old and famous Deities of Radha and Krishna. Many people would come to see these Deities and make donations for Their worship.

The guru, however, was growing weak due to old age. He knew it was time to soon leave his body but did not feel confident to hand over to his disciples the entire service of these Deities.

One day a pilgrim donated a large ruby to the Deities.

"I think it should be sold for money," one disciple declared.

"No, no!" another cried. "Radha should wear it."

Yet another gave his opinion, "It would be far better if we cut it into many small rubies. Then we could make a beautiful necklace for Her."

The disagreement among the disciples carried on for so long that the brahmin felt that the Deities would never get Their ruby. But, he did not interfere. He wanted his students to learn how to manage the ashram themselves. After a while he said, "That's enough. Now each of you go to the woods. Bring back one stick, no more than inch thick."

The seven disciples stopped their quarrelling and set out to obey their guru's order.

When they returned, the old brahmin took their sticks. He tied them all firmly together with a couple of lengths of rope. He then asked, "Which one of you can break this bundle?"

The seven young men each tried in turn, but even the strongest failed. "It's not possible," they exclaimed.

"Watch," their guru said, cutting the rope with a knife. Taking each stick on its own, he easily snapped it in two. "I am getting very old. Soon I will die. You are like a bundle of sticks. If you try to help each other, cooperate and work together, you will be strong and serve me well. But if you become divided and fight, you will become weak like these separate sticks.

And then, who will care for our Radha and Krishna Deities?"

Realising their folly, the seven disciples agreed to set the ruby in a gold ring. That ring, they decided, was to decorate one of Krishna's fingers.

Their guru, pleased at this decision, finally felt ready to leave them. Soon after, he peacefully quit his body and returned to the spiritual world.

Later, when people came to see the old brahmin's famous Deities they often asked, "How did Krishna get such a beautiful ring?"

The disciples would always answer, "By the strength of a bundle of sticks."

The King's Finger

Once upon a time there lived a king and his minister. The king, though strong and generous, possessed a short temper. His minister was wise, patient and devoted to God. In everyday affairs the king usually thought he was the one making everything happen. The minister, however, saw the hand of God everywhere. Despite these differences, the king appreciated the minister, and they were firm friends.

To protect his citizens from dangerous beasts, the king, armed with bow and arrow, would often ride into the forest with a small party of men. His minister would always go with them.

One day while they were out hunting, the king proudly charged through a thicket on his fine steed. But a large cobra slithered in front of the horse, splitting poison from its fangs. The frightened horse kicked up violently, hurtling the king through the air. The king crashed to the ground beside the snake. The snake promptly sank its fangs into the king's finger, and then slithered back into the undergrowth.

The king realised that unless his finger was quickly removed, the poison would travel through his body, reach his heart and kill him. Without hesitating, he unsheathed his sharp sword and chopped off the finger.

His minister bandaged the king's hand and tried to pacify him with wise words, "Take this as simply the mercy of the Lord. Accept it as part of His plan."

The king, shaken and upset, did not appreciate the minister's view. "Be quiet!" he snapped.

But the minister continued to speak of the Lord's mercy. This enraged the king so much that he ordered his men, "Take this foolish minister back to the city and cast him in the dungeon."

Determined not to change his hunting plan for the day, the king, his hand neatly bandaged, continued alone through the forest searching for wild beasts.

A short while later he was ambushed by a gang of bandits. They captured and bound him. Their leader, grinning broadly, spoke in a gruff voice, "This is your lucky day. I am going to sacrifice you to the Goddess Kali. It's not every day she enjoys royal blood!"

The king, however, considered himself most unlucky. Bound with ropes he had no way of saving himself from a bloody death on Kali's altar.

Pointing at the king, the leader ordered his men. "Our human offering should be stripped, washed and wrapped in new cloth."

As the dacoits stripped him, one cried out, "Look, there is a finger missing."

Inspecting the king's hand, the leader of the dacoits was disappointed. "We cannot possibly offer an incomplete human to Kali," he grunted. "Release him, you fool, and find someone else."

Unexpectedly freed from his bonds, the king mounted his horse and sped back to the city. Going straight to the dungeons, he ordered the release of his minister.

Embracing his friend, the king apologised, "By the mercy of the Lord I lost a finger. And as a result, I had my life spared!"

After explaining the incredible incident to his minister, the king paused thoughtfully, "I'm still a little puzzled. If everything that happens is the mercy of the Lord, what is the point in you being thrown in the dungeon?"

With a knowing twinkle in his eye, the minister replied, "If you hadn't ordered me to be thrown in the dungeon, I would have been with you when you were captured. Finding me with no parts missing, the Kali worshippers would undoubtedly have used me as the human offering!"

Both the king and his minister laughed loudly, tears streaming down their faces. Glad to be alive, they agreed that it certainly was all the mercy of the Lord.

The Brahmin's Daughter

There was once a poor brahmin priest who had an unmarried daughter. He was so poor that he had no money to pay for her wedding.

He also had a wife who always nagged him. "You, lazy good-for-nothing," she would shout. "All you do is sit around chanting prayers and reading scripture. Why don't you go out and do some work? Then we might be able to pay for our daughter's wedding?"

Finally, one morning she insisted, "If you don't earn enough money for our daughter's wedding by tonight, then don't bother coming back." She pushed him out of the house and slammed the door.

The brahmin was distressed. He only knew how to be a priest, and priests didn't earn very much money. But he knew that Krishna, who was famous for giving protection to brahmins, was herding cows not far away. So, he decided to seek His help.

Approaching Krishna with great respect, the brahmin said, "My dear Lord, I have come to seek Your help and protection."

Krishna's eyes widened. "And from whom am I supposed to protect you?"

The brahmin cleared his throat. "Uh, my wife. You see, our beautiful daughter cannot get married because I am so poor. My wife has threatened to throw me out if I don't return home tonight with enough money for the wedding."

The cowherd girls, standing close by, glanced lovingly at Krishna and smiled shyly. Catching their eyes, Krishna blushed a little. He shrugged His shoulders and said, "I only look after My father's cows. I have no money. So how can I help you?"

Feeling disappointed and hopeless, the brahmin stared at the ground and remained silent.

Krishna thought deeply for a minute or two. Then He said, "The scriptures say the brahmins should be given valuable gifts in charity. My most valuable possession is My favourite girlfriend, Radharani. So I give Her as a gift to you. Please take Her."

Radharani was stunned. She looked about at Her friends, who all burst into tears.

The brahmin wept also, but for a different reason. "Now I shall have two daughters to get married! I must earn even more money still." Shaking his downcast head, he moaned, "What shall I do? What shall I do?"

Feeling sorry for the brahmin, kind-hearted Radharani wiped Her eyes and whispered to Krishna, "We must help this poor man."

Krishna nodded in approval, but added, "I don't know what we can do. I cannot speak a lie, nor is it right for me to take you back after giving You as a gift."

Then, thinking for a moment, Krishna told the cowherd boys, "Bring the largest set of scales you can find."

The boys ran off and returned with a very large set of scales.

The brahmin watched in confusion as Krishna asked Radharani to sit in one side of the scales. He then asked all the cowherd boys and girls to pile up their gold bangles, pearl necklaces and other valuable ornaments until they had balanced Radharani's weight with their jewellery.

The cowherd boys and girls bundled the treasure up in a large cloth. They presented it to the brahmin. "This is much more valuable than this young girl. We would like to give it to you in exchange for Radharani."

The brahmin, beaming with happiness, leapt in the air and shouted, "God bless you all."

Although he was carrying the heavy treasure on his bank, he danced all the way home. Needless to say, his wife soon arranged a magnificent wedding for their beloved daughter, and thereafter they all lived in great happiness.

Five Blind Men and an Elephant

Along the banks of the Indus River, five men met every day under the shade of the palm trees. These men, however, could not see the gently flowing river nor the swaying green leaves, for they were all blind from birth. To pass the time they would take it in turns to tell the others the tallest story. Competing with each other, they would add all sorts of fantastic details to their fabricated stories.

One day a tame elephant wandered under the palm trees, also seeking shade. Sensing the blind men to be harmless, the creature came and stood peacefully on the river bank.

Because the men all had an acute sense of hearing, they knew that something had joined them. However, they couldn't agree what it was. So, approaching the animal, they each reached out and touched the part of the elephant nearest to them.

Feeling the elephant's body, the first man said, "It's a great mud wall that has been baked hard in the sun. how it has moved here confounds me though."

The second man touched the elephant's tusks. He exclaimed, "No, it's not a wall. What we have here are two ivory spears, no more no less."

The third man was stroking the elephant's writhing trunk. "Don't be ridiculous. This is a large leathery python hanging from a tree."

"Nonsense!" shouted the fourth man, who had grasped the elephant's tail with both hands. "It should be obvious to any sensible person that this is nothing more than a thick piece of rope."

The fifth man, who was clasping the elephant's leg, disagreed with them all. "You've all lost your sense of touch. This is as sturdy as a pillar. It can only be the trunk of a palm tree."

A small boy happened to pass by. He asked the men, "Why are you all holding that elephant?"

For once in their lives the witty men were lost for words. The boy thought to himself, "Perhaps they're deaf and dumb." And he went on his way.

As soon as he had left the blind men found their tongues again.

"It seems that we are foolish as well as blind," the first man said shamefully

"Yes," agreed the second. "We were all extremely proud to speak so boldly."

"I must admit I only guessed," confessed the third man.

"Perhaps it's better to be silent," suggested the fourth.

"But better still," concluded the fifth man, "is to learn the truth from one who directly knows it."

Vrikasura

Vrikasura, a powerful demon, could never be satisfied. He wanted power over everyone, and would do anything to get it.

In order to obtain the blessing of Lord Shiva he went to snowy Kedarnath high in the Himalaya mountains. After lighting a sacrificial fire and calling the name of Shiva he began to offer his own flesh by cutting it from his body.

Unable to attract Lord Shiva's attention he finally prepared to chop off his own head as an offering. Just then Lord Shiva appeared saying, "Please stop Vrika, I don't require your head. What is it you want?"

"I want to be able to touch anyone's head and make it shatter into a hundred pieces," the demon replied without hesitation. Lord Shiva shook his head in disbelief at the request. But he had promised to grant whatever the demon wished. Reluctantly he said, "So be it."

But Vrikasura was not satisfied just receiving this wish. He wanted to immediately test it out. So, he reached out to touch Lord Shiva's head hoping to kill him and then take his beautiful wife, Gauri.

Lord Shiva, fearing for his life, used his mystic powers to fly away. But, to wherever in the universe he fled the powerful demon was close behind.

Approaching the gods in heaven, Lord Shiva urgently begged them for protection. Alas, they could do nothing. Their answer was silence.

In great desperation Lord Shiva finally approached the planet of Lord Vishnu, the pole star. To greet Lord Shiva the all-knowing Lord Vishnu assumed the form of a young brahmacari (a student of the spiritual science). He had a radiant smiling face and wore a belt, beads and deerskin. Standing before Lord

Shiva and completely understanding the whole situation, the brahmacari assured him: "Don't worry, I will deal with this sinful demon."

Just then Vrikasura arrived and the smiling brahmacari immediately approached him saying, "My dear Vrikasura, you appear very tired. Your body is very important so please give it some rest and tell me your purpose in coming here. Perhaps I can help you in your mission."

Charmed by these sweet words, Vrikasura explained, "I want to crack Lord Shiva's head with the boon he gave me." In order to fool Vrikasura, the brahmacari spoke as follows: "O king of the demons, you should know Lord Shiva has become mad after his father-in-law, Daksha, cursed him to become a ghost. Lord Shiva's blessings are simply the words of a madman and are therefore useless. You can prove this to be true by touching your own head and, finding the benediction to be false, you can immediately kill this liar."

Bewildered by the convincing words of the boy, Vrikasura touched his own head which cracked into a hundred pieces as if struck by thunder. The demon died immediately.

Lord Vishnu in the form of a brahmacari informed Lord Shiva, "Anyone who acts offensively against a great soul cannot expect to live long. This demon died as a result of his own sins."

Thus, Lord Shiva was saved from death by the grace of Lord Vishnu. Furthermore, it is said that anyone who hears this story with faith and devotion will certainly be protected from the hands of their enemies.

Lord Chaitanya and the Banana Salesman

Kolavecha Shridhar was a great devotee of Lord Krishna but he was very poor. He sold bananas, and cups made from banana leaves, in the marketplace. He divided whatever little profit he earned equally between the care of his family and his worship of the Ganges River.

One day Lord Chaitanya, who is actually Krishna in the disguise of a devotee, came to the marketplace. He told Shridhar, "I'd like some bananas, but your price is too high."

Not recognising his Lord, Shridhar protested, "My profits go to worship of Mother Ganges. I cannot lower my prices for just anyone who comes along."

"But I can't pay that much. You must give Me a better price," begged the Lord.

"No, my price is set and that is that," insisted Shridhar.

But Lord Chaitanya would not take no for an answer. He snatched a bunch of bananas and ran away.

Shridhar yelled after Him, "Come back, you thief!" But the Lord had gone.

A few days later Chaitanya returned to the market and again asked Shridhar, "Please sir, I want to buy some bananas, but your price is too high."

Shridhar became angry. "I won't sell You bananas at any price. A few days ago, You, stole away the profit with which I worship Mother Ganges. Just who do You think You are?"

"Well, sir," Lord Chaitanya answered politely, "I am Chaitanya of Navadwip."

Shridhar stopped fuming. He considered carefully this person standing before him: tall, strong and with a delicate golden complexion. His expression was pure and happy, and His face full of knowledge and love. Shridhar concluded, "Who else can this be but Krishna in a golden form?" He then fell to the ground and prayed with all humility. "Forgive me, my Lord, I did not understand it was You, the very source of Mother Ganges. Please, take all my bananas."

Lord Chaitanya smiled broadly. Laughing, He raised Shridhar from the ground and clasped him affectionately to His chest.

In spiritual ecstasy Shridhar also began to laugh. He realised that it had been the Lord's pastime to steal his bananas.

Later on, a servant of Lord Chaitanya came to Shridhar's humble banana stand, "O fortunate devotee, the Lord wants you to join Him for a kirtan, to sing the glories of Lord Krishna with musical instruments and dance in happiness. Please come."

"Lord Chaitanya wants me to attend the Kirtan?" Shridhar exclaimed. Then he fell down in a faint. He awoke to find himself at the kirtan party, and he happily joined in with the chanting and dancing.

When the chanting finished, Lord Chaitanya took Shridhar aside. By His mystic power the Lord revealed His original form, that of Krishna, the divine cowherd boy. Sporting a peacock feather in His hair,

He stood holding a flute in His hand.

Now Shridhar could see with his own eyes that Lord Chaitanya and Lord Krishna were actually the same person. He was dumbstruck. Who could have imagined such a thing?

Lord Chaitanya then said, "I am very happy with your determination in serving Mother Ganges. When selling your bananas to Me you wouldn't budge an inch. It is exemplary that all your tiny profit goes to feed your family and to perform your worship. Now, is there anything that I can do for you?"

Shridhar felt very embarrassed. "You are my Lord. I am simply satisfied to be Your devotee. I don't need anything but that."

"Wouldn't you like to be freed from this material world and go back to the spiritual realm?" asked Lord Chaitanya."

"My Lord, I want only what You want. I am happy to stay here and make sure You get all the bananas You ask for. Please let us go on having these wonderful meetings. That is all I care about."

Lord Chaitanya was very happy with Shridhar's simple, determined mood of service. To this day Shridhar remains the Lord's devotee who eternally supplies Him bananas and banana leaf cups whenever He wants them.

The Thread and The Blanket

The mountains were cold at night and the young travellers still had several days to go before reaching the source of the sacred Ganges River. Like fallen leaves blown together in the wind, the travellers were in a mixed bunch. They often discussed the teachings of their various gurus (spiritual teachers).

One evening, as they were getting ready for bed, a pilgrim named Shivaraj said, "My guru says that everything is one. There is no difference between God and the world, or between God and the soul."

Ramdas could not agree. "Not according to my teacher, He says that even though everything comes from God, it doesn't mean that everything is God. The soul always remains separate from the Lord."

"That's your illusion!" retorted Shivaraj. "When drops of water enter the ocean they merge into the ocean. The separate drops exist no more. When you become liberated you will realise that you are God."

"On the contrary," replied Ramadas, "when the soul enters the spiritual nature it may appear to merge, but factually it never does. It is like a green parrot entering a green tree. It appears to merge but both the bird and the tree remain separate.

Similarly, even after liberation the soul remains distinct from God."

In this way the discussion went on for over an hour. "I still say that everything is God," Shivaraj said. Then pointing to the clothing beside their beds, he added, "Just as we call all our clothes by different names- shirts, pyjamas, sarees- but actually all that really exists is the thread."

Ramdas shook his head. He did not believe this.

Out to prove his point, Shivaraj pointed to his bedding. "See this blanket? It's nothing but thread going both this way and that way. There is no difference between the thread and the blanket."

Smiling broadly, Ramdas tugged at a length of loose thread on his own blanket. Then he quietly asked, "You say there is no difference between the thread and the blanket?"

"Of course," returned Shivraj, with an air of confidence, "My guru often gives this example"

"Very Well," laughed Ramdas. "Let's trade. I'll take your blanket tonight. You should be quite happy with this thread, because for you, it's the same as the blanket."

Shivaraj somewhat reluctantly handed over his only blanket.

But in the middle of the night, Ramdas was awakened by a tap on his shoulder. It was Shivaraj. "I'm freezing, could I please have my blanket back?"

"Of course," Ramdas said. "But do you still believe that everything is one?"

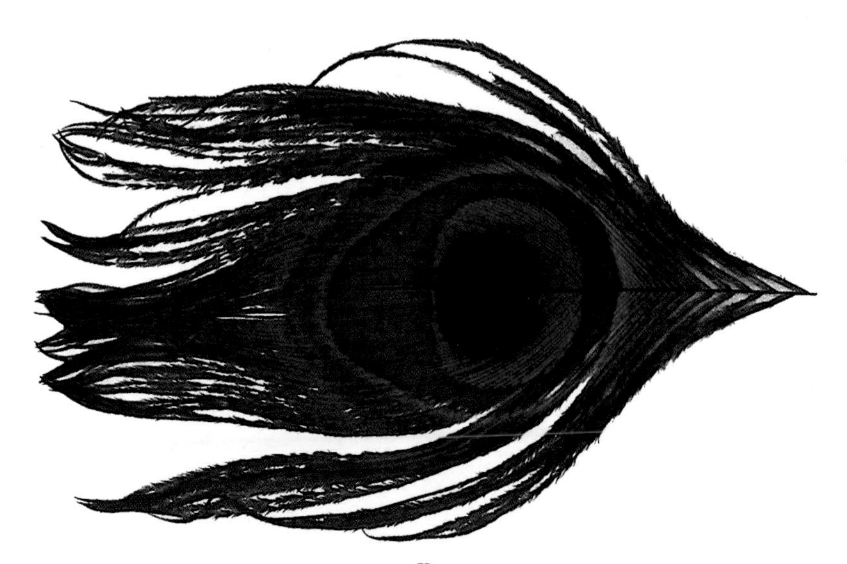

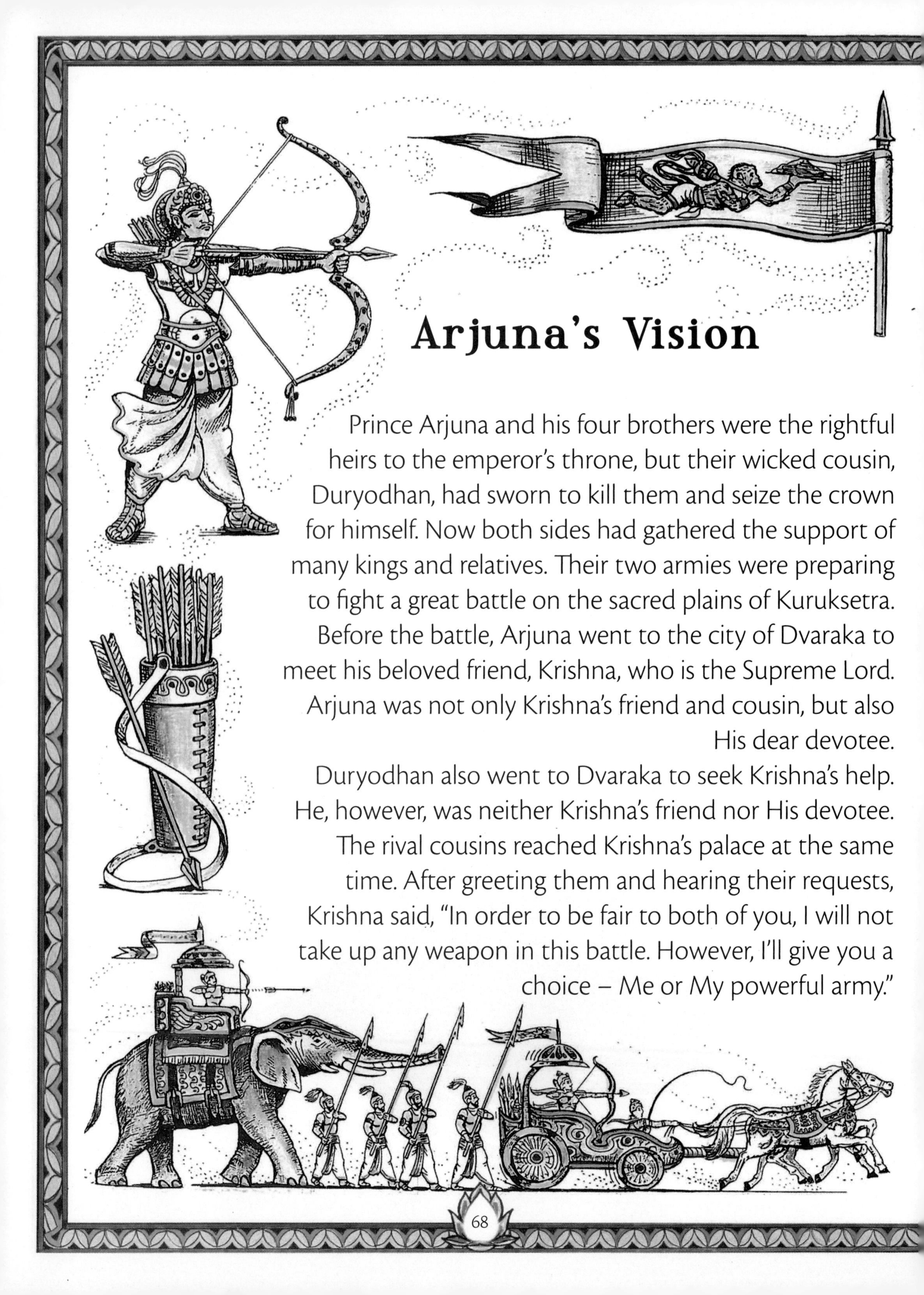

Arjuna's Vision

Prince Arjuna and his four brothers were the rightful heirs to the emperor's throne, but their wicked cousin, Duryodhan, had sworn to kill them and seize the crown for himself. Now both sides had gathered the support of many kings and relatives. Their two armies were preparing to fight a great battle on the sacred plains of Kuruksetra.

Before the battle, Arjuna went to the city of Dvaraka to meet his beloved friend, Krishna, who is the Supreme Lord. Arjuna was not only Krishna's friend and cousin, but also His dear devotee.

Duryodhan also went to Dvaraka to seek Krishna's help. He, however, was neither Krishna's friend nor His devotee.

The rival cousins reached Krishna's palace at the same time. After greeting them and hearing their requests, Krishna said, "In order to be fair to both of you, I will not take up any weapon in this battle. However, I'll give you a choice – Me or My powerful army."

Without hesitation Arjuna choose, "I want You, Krishna, to be my chariot driver."

"You do understand that I will not shoot a single arrow in your defence, don't you?" Krishna querried.

Arjuna nodded. He knew that with Krishna on his side, he could be victorious.

Duryodhan sneered. He considered Arjuna foolish for not choosing the army. He said, "I will happily take Your army."

"Then it is settled," the Lord replied.

On the battlefield Krishna drove Arjuna's chariot to the forefront of the troops. There Arjuna asked him to draw the chariot between the two armies so that he might see who was present.

Arjuna scanned the horizon: the armies stretched in all directions as far as the eye could see. It looked like a shimmering ocean with weapons and war machinery glinting and flashing, reflecting the rays of the early morning sun. on both sides the heroic warriors were dressed in colourful silks and golden ornaments. With their huge elephants and snorting horses, they moved forward to the rhythmic beat of drums. War chariots bristling with spears, maces and javelins rumbled into position carrying the mightiest soldiers on earth. Fluttering proudly from these chariots were banners displaying various emblems such as the lion, cobra and eagle. It was to be a war, the likes of which the earth had never before seen.

In the midst of both sides Arjuna saw his sons, cousins, brothers, uncles, teachers, grandsons and grandfathers. Realising that many of these relatives would be killed by his hand, Arjuna was overwhelmed with grief and sorrow. He trembled, and his hair stood on end.

Arjuna had a magical bow, called Gandiva, which shot lightning-fast arrows, so powerful that they could even block the flow of a river. He now cast that bow aside and lamented the uselessness of the war. "I cannot fight and kill my relatives."

He held his head in his hands and admitted to Krishna, "I am confused about my duty. Please tell me what to do."

Krishna smiled upon him kindly. "Arjuna, don't you know that those who are wise don't lament- neither for the living nor for the dead? For the soul there is never both nor death. He is eternal and not slain when the body is slain. The soul can never be cut by weapons. Therefore, do not grieve, but do your duty and be saved from dishonour."

Arjuna looked up at his friend. "Tell me more."

"Arjuna, you don't need to fear. This whole creation is under My control; I create and destroy it again and again. I am ever-lasting life and death itself. Yet all the gods in heaven do not know where I come from, for I am the very source of the gods.

The wise who know this are My devotees and they worship Me with all their hearts."

Krishna's soothing words of wisdom had a wonderful effect on Arjuna, whose attention shifted from the battlefield to Krishna's beautiful features. He begged, "O Krishna, you are the Lord of the universe. Please tell me in detail of Your divine powers."

Lord Krishna explained how He exhibits His power and glory through the wondrous features of nature- the light of the sun, the power of the ocean and the beauty of spring. He concluded, "O mighty conqueror of enemies, Arjuna, know that all beautiful, glorious and mighty creations spring from but a spark of My splendour."

Arjuna was elated to hear this and requested Krishna, "O my Lord, if You think I am able to behold it, please show me Your universal form."

The Lord agreed, saying, "Behold now My hundreds and thousands of divine forms, numerous like the waves of the ocean. Whatever you wish to see can be seen at once in this body; everything is here completely. But you cannot see it with your present eyes. Therefore, I grant you divine eyes by which you can behold My glory."

Arjuna watched as Krishna's body grew to a colossal size, His hundreds of arms, legs, heads, and eyes covering all directions. It was fearful to look at. Adorned with dazzling ornaments the Lord looked like thousands of suns rising in the sky at the same time. Then, as if in a vivid dream, Arjuna saw all the enemy soldiers from the opposite side rushing like rivers into the blazing mouths of that form.

Krishna solemnly spoke, "I am Time, the destroyer of the worlds. Know that all your enemies will be slain. I want you to get up and prepare to fight. Take credit for what has already been arranged by Me."

His mind reeling from such a frightening vision, Arjuna implored Krishna to appear again as the smiling friend he knew so well. And Krishna, out of kindness to His devotee, reassumed His original form.

Arjuna felt strengthened and inspired by this vision which he alone was privileged to see. "My confusion and weakness are now gone. By Your mercy I am free from doubt and fear." Reaching for his Gandiva bow he declared, "I will act accordingly to Your instruction."

With Krishna by his side, Arjuna knew that victory was already his.

The Crow And The Tal Fruit

Manu, a young devotee of Krishna, stopped at the edge of town along the banks of a winding river. Manu had been walking for many days and had several more to go before reaching the holy town of Vrindavan.

After looking up and down the river he decided on the most suitable place to cross. But before doing so, with hands together in prayer, he sought permission from the river goddess. He then respectfully sprinkled a palmful of her water over his head and began to cross, at first hopping from rock to rock and then wading the rest of the way.

Upon reaching the trees on the opposite bank he heard raised voices. As he went closer he saw a group of pandits (scholars) arguing about where we have all come from in the beginning of time. Each one was trying to present that he knew best by using big words and quoting from scripture.

Suddenly, a shrieking crow flew from one of the palm trees under which the men were standing. At the same time a large tal fruit fell on the ground before them.

The pandits were startled. Then one exclaimed, "What a coincidence! The bird flies from a tree and a fruit drops at exactly the same time. It's amazing how randomly chance works."

"Nonsense!" another said, thrusting his bearded chin forward, obviously proud of his intelligence. "Nothing happens by chance. Everything happens as a result of something else. The tal fruit obviously fell to the ground because the crow tried to land on it."

"That's just pure guesswork," a third scholar scoffed. "Gravity made the fruit fall. As a result, the startled bird flew away."

One after another the pandits argued about what had happened- but they could not agree. Each thought that he knew best.

Quite amused by their exchanges, young Manu stepped forward. "Excuse me gentlemen, I've been listening to you all with great interest. It's surprising that such learned men are unable to come to an agreement over such a simple matter."

The pandits fell silent. So, Manu continued, "If you allow me, I can settle this matter for you very easily."

Still silent, the pandits nodded, and Manu entered their circle, siting near the fallen fruit. "You all agree that not a blade of grass moves without the consent of the Lord, do you not?"

The men nodded in agreement.

"Therefore," Manu said, "the bird flew, and the fruit fell, both by the will of the Lord. Which caused which is irrelevant."

"Yes, yes!" the pandits agreed. Then Manu dipped the fruit in the river to wash it. He said, "The all-powerful Lord accepts fruit, water, flowers or even leaves if they are offered with love and devotion. So, I'm going to offer this fruit to Him. Then we can enjoy it as prasad, His mercy." He then broke the fruit open and offered it to God with prayers.

Dividing it among the pandits, he said, "Isn't it more sensible to do something positive in the present than to argue about the past?"

Their mouths full of juicy fruits, the pandits agreed. One even said, "As long as we know the purpose of our lives, what does it matter where we come from?"

The Gift Of The Sun God

The five Pandava princes were heirs to the throne of the world. Duryodhan, their envious cousin, was always scheming how to get rid of them so he could claim the crown for himself. Killing the Pandavas, though, was not so easy, for Lord Krishna was their special friend. And everyone knew that Krishna's powers were unlimited.

However, by cheating at a gambling match, Duryodhan managed to banish his cousins to the forest for thirteen years. They took with them Draupadi, the devoted and beautiful wife of all five brothers.

To assist the Pandavas during their exile, the Sun God gave Draupadi a special pot as a gift. With it she could always feed her own family as well as an unlimited number of guests. The only rule was that after Draupadi had eaten

for that day, the magical pot would produce no more food until the next. So, even though they were living in the forest, the Pandavas were never hungry.

Duryodhan and his brothers often spied on the Pandavas during their exile in the forest. And one day, while camping nearby, Duryodhan was visited by a famous mystic yogi, Durvasa. Durvasa was very quick-tempered. If he ever became angry he would put dreadful curses on people. And if he were pleased, he was quick to offer benedictions as well.

On this particular visit, Durvasa was not alone. He had come with ten thousand disciples. Duryodhan was crafty as well as evil-hearted. So, he was exceedingly careful to welcome the great saint with the utmost care and attention. He personally made sure that whenever Durvasa said he was hungry, even in the middle of the night, food was brought to him.

The yogi was obviously pleased with Duryodhan' service, and after a few days he said, "Ask me for a benediction. I'll give you whatever you desire."

Duryodhan was elated. This was just what he had hoped would happen. But he didn't want to let the yogi know that his desire was for something very wicked, so very innocently he said, "You are very kind. The only thing I would like is for my beloved cousins, the Pandavas, to have the pleasure of your company. By good fortune they are staying not far from here. I simply desire that you visit them."

Durvasa agreed to this simple request. Duryodhan watched as the sage and his ten thousand disciples departed. He chuckled to himself, thinking, "The Pandavas have taken lunch already. Now they'll never be able to feed Durvasa and all his disciples. I can't imagine what kind of terrible curse he will cast upon them."

The eldest Pandava, Yudisthira, along with his brothers, greeted Durvasa and his men when they reached the camp. It was a shock for the princes to see so many guests. As the entourage walked into the camp, Yudisthira turned to Draupadi and whispered, "Quick! Get your magic pot so we can offer them something to eat."

"But I have already eaten", she confessed. "The pot is now empty until tomorrow."

After exchanging a few polite words with the sage, Yudisthira requested, "My dear Durvasa, you've been walking for so long in the forest. Please go and bathe. When you return, your meal will be waiting for you."

Durvasa and his disciple happily made their way to the river. The Pandavas, meanwhile, were in a panic. They knew of Durvasa's reputation; of how he was so easily upset, and of the power of his curse. Draupadi was in tears. In that condition, she did the only thing she knew could possibly help. From the depths of her heart she called on Lord Krishna. "O master of the universe, O Lord of the Gods, please protect us. Without You we are lost."

Miraculously, as if from nowhere, Krishna appeared before her. He listened as Draupadi explained the whole situation, but He did not offer a solution. Instead He said, "I am hungry, Draupadi. Would you please bring Me some food?"

Bewildered, Draupadi replied, "But I've already told You, the pot the Sun God gave me is empty. It won't yield any more food today. Now I have two problems: I cannot feed You, nor can I feed Durvasa and his followers."

Krishna merely smiled. "Don't worry. Just bring Me the pot."

Still puzzled, Draupadi fetched the pot and Krishna inspected it closely. "Oh, this looks delicious," Krishna said, having discovered a morsel of vegetable stuck on the rim. Taking it between His fingers He popped it in His mouth.

Then he requested Bheema, the strongest of the Pandava princes to call Durvasa and his men from the river. "Tell them their meal is ready."

As Bheema approached the riverside he saw Durvasa and the other sages standing waist-deep in the water. They were all doing a very curious thing: they were rubbing their bellies as if they were filled with food.

Bheema then heard Durvasa say, "Oh no! Look! Here comes Bheema carrying a club. If we insult him by refusing to eat what Draupadi has prepared, he will be furious. But how can we eat? We're all feeling completely satisfied. I can't eat anything, no matter how delicious it is."

Bheema could hardly believe his eyes and ears. Durvasa's ten thousand disciples were all saying, "Me too! I can't even think about eating now." Then, as Bheema got closer, they all ran into the forest, still wet from their bath, and only half-dressed. Bheema laughed and ran back to tell the other Pandava princes. Much to their relief, the guests never returned.

Draupadi said, "I realise what has happened. If you water the roots of a tree then its other parts- the twigs, leaves, branches, and flowers- are all benefitted. Krishna is like the root of a tree. So when Krishna is satisfied, everyone is satisfied, including Durvasa and his thousands of followers.

Through Draupadi's devotion and the kindness of Lord Krishna, the Pandavas were saved from Duryodhana's evil plans.

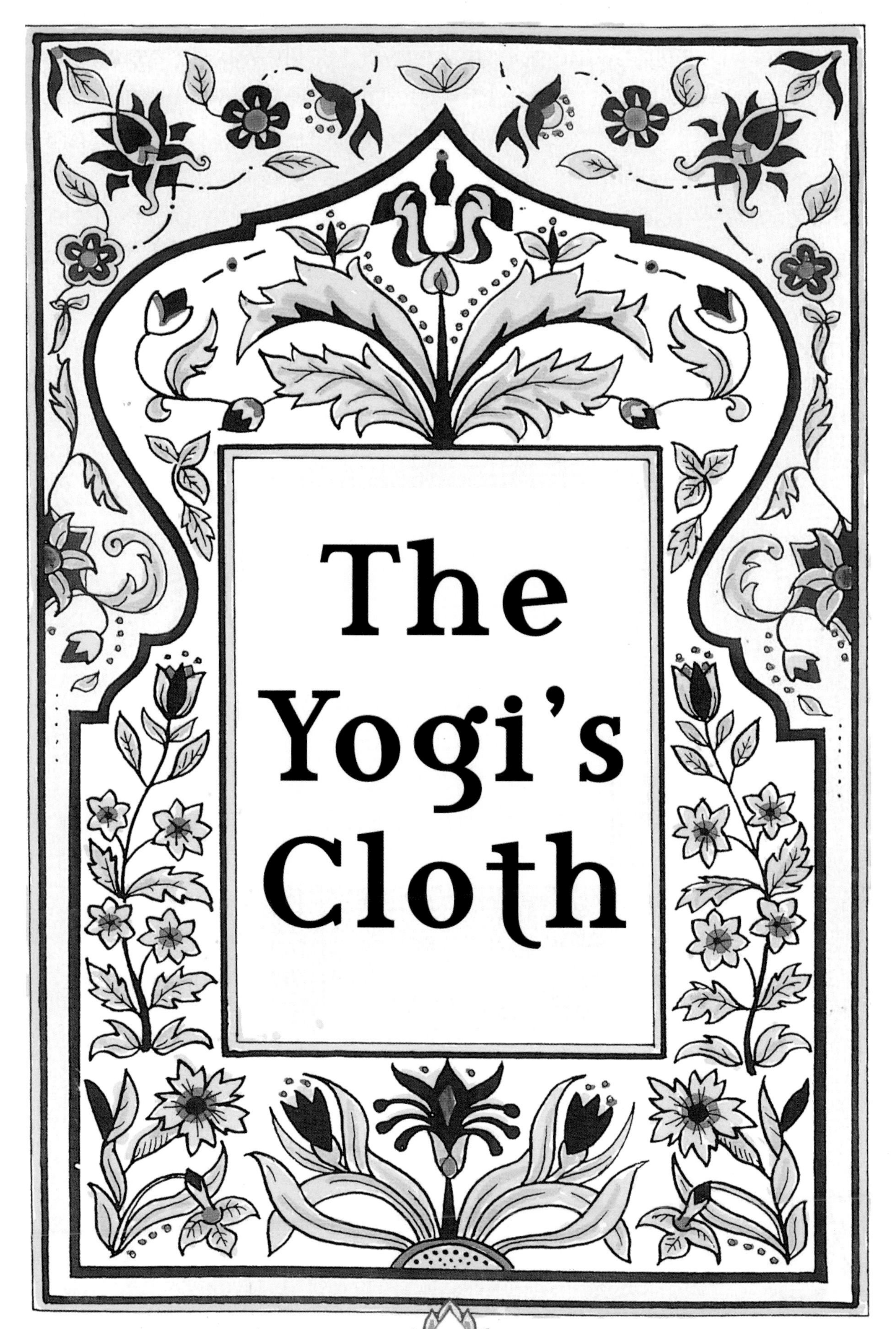

The Yogi's Cloth

A young yogi lived by the side of the river. His life was simple and carefree; he practised yoga almost all-day long. Because he had no other responsibilities, he had plenty of time to sit peacefully with closed eyes, his thoughts fixed on the Lord within the heart. This was his daily meditation.

One day, after bathing in the river, he washed his only piece of cloth and lay it out on the rocky bank. While waiting for it to dry, a thought crossed his mind, "I am wasting time waiting for this. If I had another piece of cloth I could get dressed right away."

Just then an old sadhu (a wise man) passed by. This sadhu was able to read the thoughts of others. He stopped and spoke with the young yogi. "My dear son, I know what is on your mind. You want to save time. But rather than collecting more and more possessions, it's better to be happy with what you have." He then offered the yogi his blessings and continued on his way.

The young yogi pondered the sadhu's advice but decided that just one extra cloth was not too much to desire. So, he went to the marketplace and bought one.

The next day he bathed in the river as usual, washed his cloth, and put it on the rock to dry. Then he put on his nice new cloth and went to perform his meditation.

Later in the day, when he came back, he discovered that a hungry mouse had nibbled holes in his old cloth. At first, he was dismayed, but then thought, "I know! I'll get a cat to chase away the mouse."

He went to the market once again and bought a cat.

He spent the next day very happily and peacefully meditating. But, as evening approached, the cat began to meow, disturbing the yogi.

"Oh, he needs milk," he groaned. And so, he reluctantly left for the market again, returning this time with a cow.

The next day was peaceful until the evening when the cow began to moo. "I'm not going to milk it every day!" thought the yogi. "It takes too much time."So, he went to the village and asked a young woman to be his wife. She could get milk from the cow to give to the cat, who would keep the mouse away from the yogi's cloth.

And so, the yogi was happy for a while.

One evening his wife complained, "I'm sick of you just meditating all day. I want a home."

So the yogi built a house.

But then his wife was lonely and wanted children...

As time went by the yogi meditated less and less and worried more and more. He was constantly busy looking after his house, his growing family and the animals. Sometimes, when he had a quiet moment, he would reflect on those carefree times when all he had was a single cloth.

One day he was thinking like this when the old sadhu again passed by. The sadhu smiled and remarked, "I can see you are in a pensive mood, so I will tell you again that it's better to be happy with what you have. Because when it comes to wanting things, there is no end."

Lord Jagannath and the Proud Merchant

The Lord of the Universe, Jagannath, lives in His temple at Puri, in the state of Orissa. There He is worshipped in great style with His brother, Balaram, and His sister, Subhadra.

All the people of Puri love Jagannath more than their very lives: indeed, He is their very reason for living. They are devoted to Him and He, in turn, is devoted to them, granting them all protections. To this very day, even the King of Orissa is happy to consider himself the humble servant of Jagannath. On the day of Lord Jagannath's annual chariot festival, the king sweeps the road before the Lord's chariot with a golden-handled broom.

Along with prayers and worship, Jagannath daily accepts regular offerings of foods. The cooks and priests at Jagannath's temple are always busy making and offering foodstuffs prepared from fruit, milk, grains and vegetables.

One day a wealthy merchant came to visit the temple, more out of curiosity than devotion. Blinded by pride, he considered Jagannath to be simply a strange wooden statue with a black smiling face and large round eyes. Just to upset the temple priests he said, "I would like to offer one hundred thousand rupees to cover the cost of one food offering." The priests all smiled at his generosity.

"But only on one condition," the merchant continued. "Every last rupee must be used."

The priests were puzzled. Even using the most expensive ghee, and making the best coconut and milk sweets, a lot of money would still be left over. They felt it would certainly be a shame to refuse the offer, but how could they honestly accept it?

Finding no solution to the problem, all the priests gathered together and prayed to Jagannath. The panda, or head priest, offered a special prayer, "Dear Lord, please tell us what type of food to buy for you."

The wealthy merchant, intending to leave Puri the following day, insisted on a decision by sunrise. The panda, however, begged him to stay until Jagannath Himself gave the answer. This made the man feel very important, so he agreed to stay.

Three days later, Jagannath spoke to the head priest in a dream. And in the morning the panda delivered the message to the merchant.

The priest said, "Lord Jagannath says that you should pay for one betel leaf and nut made into the preparation called paan."

The man said, "This is ridiculous. I have offered to give one hundred thousand rupees. But a paan leaf and betel nut cost next to nothing."

The priest held his hand up to stop the man. "That is not all that the Lord has requested. He asked that you smear the betel nut that is laid within the betel leaf with finely ground pearl powder."

"That is more like it," the man said, nodding his head.

Once again, the priest held up his hand. "There is one other thing. The Lord does not want you to use an ordinary pearl. He asked that you obtain an extremely rare pearl to be found under the skin of an elephant's forehead."

The man's heart almost stopped beating. The colour drained from his face. He stood still for some moments, considering the meaning of the message. Then he cried, "How many elephants will I have to buy to find such a pearl? At least hundreds, if not thousands. And just one elephant costs thousands upon thousands of rupees!"

The merchant threw down his expensive silk turban and kicked off his sandals. He said, "I am unable to even offer a single betel nut to Jagannath."

Then he fell before Lord Jagannath, begging for forgiveness. "I am so foolish," he wept. "Only You, the Supreme Lord, could teach me such a lesson. Therefore, I accept You as Lord of the Universe. Everything belongs to You, so what can I possibly offer? The only thing I have is my heart. Please accept it, my Lord."

From that day on, the merchant was a changed man. Instead of being mean and arrogant, he was kind and considerate. He always gave any extra money he had to holy men and the poor.

Krishna The Cowherd Boy

In order to give pleasure to His devotees, Lord Krishna came down from the spiritual world as a human child. He appeared in a community of cowherders in the village of Vrindavan in northern India. He was adopted into the family of King Nanda and Mother Yasoda. Without exception all the villagers loved Him.

One day Krishna and His cowherd boyfriends took the calves out to the pasturing grounds. While the calves enjoyed grazing, the boys sang, danced and played games. They imitated the monkeys, frogs and peacocks, and decorated themselves with bright feathers and forest flowers.

After hours of roaming the beautiful forest, the boys and calves became tired and made their way down to the sandy banks of the River Yamuna. The thirsty calves eagerly drank from the clear flowing water and chewed the sweet grasses.

From His belt Krishna took His famous bamboo flute. He played it in such an enchanting way that the river ran backwards, and birds fell from the sky in spiritual happiness. The calves became stunned, standing as if frozen, as they listened with pricked-up ears. Even the stones began to melt in ecstasy.

Finding a shady spot on the river bank, the boys opened their lunch baskets. They had so many delicious preparations made from milk, fruit, grains, sugar and vegetables, which they spread out on leaves, rocks and pieces of tree bark. The boys sat in a circle around Krishna and shared their food with Him. They laughed and joked as they enjoyed their forest lunch.

Bakasura The Stork Demon

Years before Krishna was born, the wicked King Kamsa heard a voice from the sky warning him that one day Krishna would kill him. Kamsa was always fearful of this prediction. When Krishna was born Kamsa sent many demons to Vrindavan to destroy Him. One of these mystic demons, Bakasura, assumed the shape of a gigantic stork, as big as a hill, with a long sharp beak and evil piercing eyes.

One day, as Krishna and the cowherd boys wandered along the river bank, they saw this huge bird, Bakasura spread his enormous wings and opened his beak. Then he leapt at Krishna and swallowed Him whole.

The cowherd boys almost fainted with shock as they watched.

However, once inside Bakasura's throat, Krishna became fiery hot. So hot that that the demon had to spit Him out.

Greatly angered, Bakasura snapped at Krishna again.

But Krishna caught each of the demon's beaks and split him in two, much as a child splits a blade of grass.

Relieved that the demon was now dead, the cowherd boys embraced Krishna in great happiness. The residents of heaven showered flower petals in appreciation of the Lord's wonderful deeds.

GOVINDA
ASD

The Kaliya Serpent

All summer long the cowherd boys took the calves to different places to graze. One day they were all feeling very hot and thirsty, so they went to the Yamuna River.

Unknown to them, deep within water lurked a huge and horrible serpent called Kaliya. Kaliya had one hundred heads. He so polluted the water that the grass and trees on the river banks had all dried up. A thin cloud of poisonous mist hung over the water, spelling certain death for all who breathed it. The only living plant left on the river bank was a kadamba tree with beautiful yellow flowers. The reason why that tree could live there and not others was that Garuda, the king of birds, knew that Krishna would need this tree. So, he protected it by pouring life-saving nectar on its roots.

But the boys were very thirsty and unaware of any danger, they eagerly drank the water. As soon as they took one sip, they slumped to the ground.

After this, Krishna and his brother Balaram came to the river bank. They saw all Their friends lying there, as if dead. Krishna felt He had to get to the cause of the problem. He climbed high into the Kadamba tree. From that vantage point Krishna could see the nasty snake Kaliya sleeping in the middle of the river's water.

Balaram watched as His brother tightened His orange belt. Then Krishna flapped His arms and leapt from the treetop. He landed in the water with so much force that the river overflowed its banks. Krishna splashed about like great elephant in order to attract the terrible snake's attention.

"How dare You disturb me," Kaliya hissed. He furiously rushed at Krishna, grabbing Him in his massive coils.

For two hours Balaram watched as Krishna appeared to struggle in Kaliya's grip. During this time the whole village of Vrindavan, including Krishna's mother and father, arrived at the river bank. Struck with horror, they all watched the battle.

The villagers shivered in fear as the sky filled with terrible omens portending great danger: the earth trembled, and meteors fell from the sky. Some villagers fainted in fright. But not Balaram. He was smiling, confident that Krishna would win.

When Kaliya caught Krishna in his dangerous coils, Krishna would expand His body, and then quickly reduce His size. Thus, He easily slipped away from the snake.

The serpent was getting more and more angry. His eyes blazed like red-hot coals and he spat fire from his one hundred mouths. Flaring his hoods, he would snort poisonous fumes from his nostrils. He moved slowly in a circle, striking out with his many heads and trying to sink his fangs into Krishna's bluish body.

But, smiling constantly, Krishna merrily leapt from hood to hood, crushing each one down with His dancing feet.

Repeatedly beaten, Kaliya's heads each vomited blood. He was forced to admit defeat.

Kaliya's wives, the Nagapatnis, came from their watery residence and prayed to Krishna to have mercy upon their husband.

Pleased by their sincere prayers, Krishna ordered the serpent, "Kaliya, take your wives, family and everything you possess to the great ocean. Never come back to this river."

Kaliya said, "I have taken shelter of this Yamuna River because I am afraid of the giant eagle, Garuda. He eats snakes like me. He is your servant, so I know that he would never kill anything that lives in Vrindavan. If I move to the ocean he will certainly swoop down and kill me."

Krishna raised his hand as if to assure Kaliya, "Don't worry about him. When he sees the marks of My feet on your heads he will leave you alone."

Krishna then touched all His friends and calves who were still lying motionless on the river bank. Just the touch of His hand brought them back to life.

Seeing Krishna safe and moving amongst them, everyone was happy. They praised Him over and over again for His wonderful activities.

Dhenukasura, the Ass Demon

The cowherd boys were taking their calves to graze in the forest. This particular day one cowherd boy told Krishna and His brother, Balaram, "You are both so strong and expert in killing demons. Do You know that we are very near Talavan Forest?"

Another cowherd boy clapped his hands and exclaimed, "Oh yes! The trees there are full of fruits which are so ripe we can smell them from here."

However, another cowherd boy piped up, "But Krishna, we're frightened to go there."

"Why are you so afraid?" Krishna asked.

A small cowherd boy stepped forward. He said, "It's because of that demon Dhenukasura. He and his friends have disguised them-

selves as wild asses and have taken over the whole forest. We don't dare go there, unless You come with us."

Tugging on Krishna and Balaram's arms, all the cowherd boys pleaded, "Please come with us. Let us enjoy the fruits."

So, laughing and joking all the way, Krishna and Balaram led the boys and calves to Talavan forest. Then, upon entering the forest, They astounded Their friends by shaking the trees with Their powerful arms, just as elephants do. Many sweet, juicy fruits fell to the forest floor.

Dhenukasura, of course, heard the fruit falling. Enraged, the ass galloped to the spot with such force that the ground shook. He went straight for Balaram, striking out with his hard hooves.

Balaram, however, was not caught off guard. He simply caught the demon by his back legs and then spun him around so fast that Dhenukasura lost his life's breath.

Then Balaram casually flung Dhenukasura's dead body into the treetops. It hit with such force that other trees fell against each other like a row of falling dominos.

Seeing and hearing this, the other asses came from their hiding places in the forest. They also tried to attack Krishna and Balaram. The cowherd boys watched and cheered as Krishna and Balaram killed each one of them, flinging the dead bodies.

The Rasa Dance

One evening during the autumn season, Krishna, the divine cowherd boy, watched the beautiful full moon rise on the eastern horizon. The whole sky was tinted red and the forest flowers filled the atmosphere with their cooling fragrances.

Prompted by the appearances of the moon, Krishna desired to enjoy the company of His beloved cowherd girls, the gopis. He knew they had previously worshipped the goddess Katyayani, hoping to get Him as their husband. Now was the time, He thought, to answer their prayers.

So in a beautiful grove within the Vrindavan forest, Krishna played His enchanting flute. The magical notes of that famous flute entered the ears of the gopis and pierced their tender hearts. Though busy milking cows, serving food to their families, or applying make-up to their faces, the gopis became stunned upon hearing the flute. With an intense desire to be with Krishna, they dropped everything and ran to the grove.

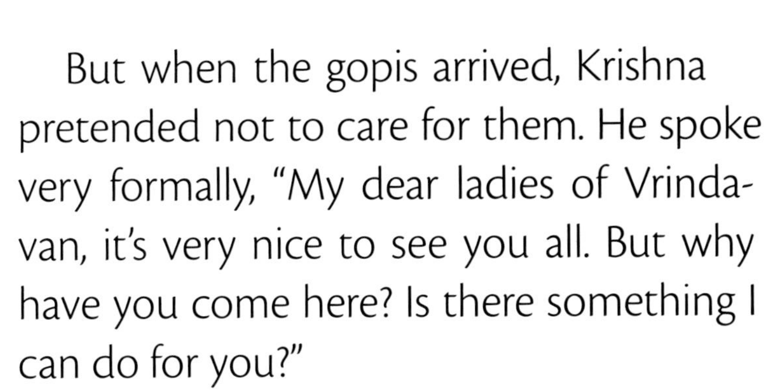

But when the gopis arrived, Krishna pretended not to care for them. He spoke very formally, "My dear ladies of Vrindavan, it's very nice to see you all. But why have you come here? Is there something I can do for you?"

The gopis smiled bashfully.

"My dear friends," Krishna continued, "the night forest is full of prowling beasts. Surely your families are worried and searching for you. I think it best that you return home right now."

The gopis, who had all given their hearts completely to Krishna, replied, "O Krishna, how can You reject us? We are completely dependent on You. We love no one but You. It is wrong for You to tell us to go."

Seeing the gopis' determination and their love for Him, Krishna changed His mood. He took them all down to the soft, sandy shores of the River Yamuna. There, in

the light of the full moon, they relaxed, joked and shared many loving moments.

After some time, however, the gopis started feeling proud that they were the lucky ones to be with Krishna. And Krishna, seeing their pride, disappeared.

Heartbroken, the gopis searched everywhere for the Lord of their heart. Throwing their arms in the air, they called out His name. they even begged the trees to reveal where He was hiding.

Unable to tolerate their loss, the gopis kept Krishna with them by play-acting His pastimes. They imitated His flute-playing and His killing various demons like Agha and Aristasura. One gopi raised her shawl over the heads of her friends and said, "Don't be afraid of the torrents of rain and the severe hurricanes. I'll save you." In this way she imitated the way Krishna had lifted Govardhan Hill as an umbrella for the villagers and their animals.

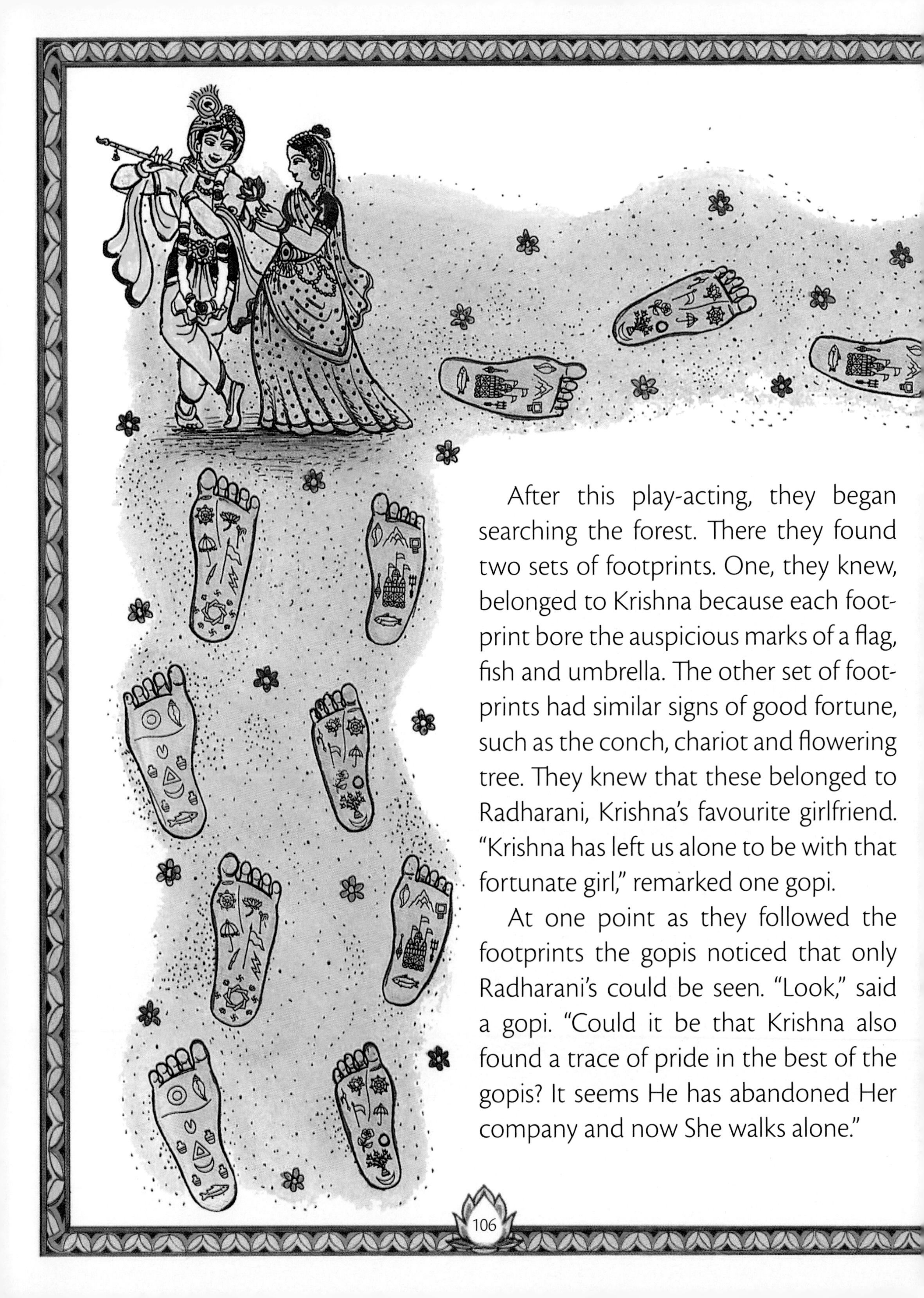

After this play-acting, they began searching the forest. There they found two sets of footprints. One, they knew, belonged to Krishna because each footprint bore the auspicious marks of a flag, fish and umbrella. The other set of footprints had similar signs of good fortune, such as the conch, chariot and flowering tree. They knew that these belonged to Radharani, Krishna's favourite girlfriend. "Krishna has left us alone to be with that fortunate girl," remarked one gopi.

At one point as they followed the footprints the gopis noticed that only Radharani's could be seen. "Look," said a gopi. "Could it be that Krishna also found a trace of pride in the best of the gopis? It seems He has abandoned Her company and now She walks alone."

The gopis followed Radharani's footprints and found Her alone and crying. Thinking only of Krishna, they all chanted His glories, praying that soon He would return to their company.

Seeing the gopis now free of all pride, Lord Krishna reappeared in their midst, smiling beautifully. Gently taking the hands of those humble souls, Krishna, like the bright moon among many stars, led them to soft white sands along the river bank. There they danced together, losing all track of time. Krishna multiplied Himself so each gopi thought that she alone was dancing with her lover. Under the light of the moon, peacocks, deer and other animals of the forest came to watch the dancing. The residents of heaven, riding in their celestial airplanes, also appeared in the sky to see this wonderful event called the rasa dance.

Glossary

A

Agni	The demigod in charge of fire
Ahimsa	Non-violence
Akbar	A Mogul emperor of medieval India
Anjana	Hanuman's mother
Anjaneya	'Son of Anjana' – one of Hanuman's names
Arjuna	The third of the Pandava brothers, begotten in Kunti by Indra, the king of the demigods. He is the intimate friend of Krishna, to whom the Lord spoke the Bhagavad Gita.

B

Bakasura	The name of the stork demon killed by Krishna
Balaram	Krishna's older brother
Basyacharya	Yamunacharya's teacher
Benaras	A holy city on the River Ganges in Northern India
Betel	A climbing plant, the leaf and seed of which are used in making paan
Bheema	The second of the Pandava brothers, begotten in Kunti by Vayu, the Wind god.
Birbal	Emperor Akbar's chief minister
Bo	The species of tree under which Lord Buddha attained enlightenment
Brahma	The demigod in charge of creation
Brahmacari	A male celibate student of spiritual science
Brahmin	The spiritual order of society
Bhrigu	Brahma's son, and a famous sage in ancient times
Brihaspati	The spiritual teacher of the demigods
Buddha	The incarnation of Krishna who preached non-violence

C

Chaitanya	The incarnation of Radha and Krishna together who popularised the chanting of the Hare Krishna mantra and opposed the hereditary caste system.
D	
Dacoit	An armed robber or bandit
Demigods	One of the beings who is subservient to the Supreme Lord and who takes on an administrative role within the universe on the Lord's behalf. It also refers more generally to the residents of the celestial realms.
Dharma	Religion or religious duty. Also a name for Yama, the lord of death, and father of Yudisthira
Dhenukasura	The ass demon killed by Balaram
Draupadi	The daughter of King Drupada and wife of the five Pandava brothers
Durvasa	A famous yogi, considered a partial incarnation of Lord Shiva
Duryodhan	The eldest son of Dhritarashtra and cousin of the Pandavas
Dwaraka	The city of Lord Krishna, situated under the ocean off the west coast of India
G	
Gandiva	The name of Arjuna's famous archery bow
Ganges	The longest of the sacred rivers of India, rising in the Himalayas and flowing to the Bay of Bengal
Garuda	The bird who transports Lord Vishnu
Gaya	A holy city in Northern India
Gopi	A cowherd girl
Govardhan	The hill which Krishna lifted to protect the inhabitants of Vrindavan
Guru	A teacher, usually a spiritual teacher
H	
Hanuman	The monkey-warrior who served Lord Rama
Himalayas	The highest mountain range in the world, in Northern India
Indra	The king of heaven and the demigod in charge of rain
Indus	The river after which India was named. It now flows in Pakistan

Jara	The daughter of Time
Jagannatha	The form of Krishna worshipped in Puri. The English word "Juggernaut" is derived from this, referring to the huge carts used in the annual festival for the Deities.
Jaya	An exclamation meaning "all glories to!", "victory"

K

Kailash	Mountain in the Himalayas considered the home of Lord Shiva
Kali	A particularly fierce form of Durga (Parvati)
Kaliya	The snake demon who polluted the River Yamuna and was punished by Krishna
Kamsa	The wicked king of Mathura who tried to kill Krishna but was ultimately killed by Him
Katyayani	A name of Parvati, Shiva's consort
Keshari	The king who adopted Hanuman as his son
Kirtan	Glorification of the Supreme Lord; specifically refers to the chanting of Krishna's names with musical instruments
Kishkinda	A forest in India
Kolahala	The court pandit Yamunacharya defeated
Kolavecha Shridhar	A humble banana seller who was a devotee of Krishna and an associate of Lord Chaitanya
Krishna	The Supreme Personality of Godhead
Kunti	Co-wife of King Pandu and mother of the first three Pandava brothers
Kurukshetra	A pilgrimage site from ancient times; the place where the Pandavas fought a battle against the Kurus
Kuvera	The demigods' treasurer

L

Lila	"Pastime"- refers to any activity performed out of free will rather than under obligation

M

Madri	Co-wife of King Pandu and mother of Nakula and Sahadeva
Mahaloka	A planet in the heavenly realm

Manu-Samhita	One of the lawbooks of mankind, compiled by Manu
Maya	Buddha's mother

N

Nagapatnis	Wife of the Kaliya serpent
Nakula	One of the Pandava princes. Madri is his mother and Sahadeva his twin brother
Namaste	A form of greeting usually offered with folded hands: "My respectful obeisances unto you."
Nanda	Krishna's father
Narada Muni	The sage amongst the demigods who can travel anywhere as he likes
Narayana	A name for the four-armed feature of the Supreme Lord

O

Odhisa	A state in Eastern India, just south of Bengal

P

Paan	A mild intoxicant made using betel nut and spices
Panda	A head priest in a temple
Pandavas	The five sons of King Pandu
Pandu	The Emperor of India some five thousand years ago
Pandit	A learned scholar
Parvati	Wife of Lord Shiva. She also has many other names
Puri	A holy city on the east coast of India in the state of Orissa

R

Radha (Radharani)	The consort of Lord Krishna
Rama (Ramachandra)	The seventh incarnation of Krishna who killed the evil king Ravana
Ramdas	A Hindu name which literally means "The servant of Rama"
Rasa	A circle dance
Rupee	Indian unit of currency.

S

Sadhu	A holy person
Sage	A wise person

Sahadeva — One of the five Pandava princes and twin brother of Nakula

Sannyasi — A wandering mendicant

Shiva — The demigod in charge of destruction

Shivaraj — An Indian name which refers to Lord Shiva

Shrutidhara — An Indian name which means "One who has a photographic memory"

Shuddhodana — A king who was Buddha's father

Siddhartha — The name given to Lord Buddha when he was a child

Subhadra — Krishna's sister

T

Tal — A type of fruit, somewhat like a coconut

V

Vanaras — A race of monkey-like people

Vayu — The demigod in charge of air

Vishnu — The all-pervading Supreme Lord who maintains this material world

Vishnuloka — The planet in the spiritual realm on which Lord Vishnu lives

Vrikasura — The demon who tried to trick Lord Shiva

Vrindavan — The village in which Krishna was brought up, one of the most important only towns in modern India

W

Wesak — The main Buddhist festival celebrated each year

Y

Yaksha — A sorcerer

Yamuna — A branch of the Ganges River, considered by many to be the holiest of rivers

Yamunacharya — A great spiritual teacher whose foremost disciple was Ramanujacharya

Yasoda — Krishna's mother

Yogi — One who practices yoga

Yudisthira — The eldest of five Pandava brothers who became the Emperor of the world, the son of Kunti and Yamaraja